An Introduction

to Equilibrium Thermodynamics

An Introduction

to Equilibrium

Thermodynamics

Robert P. Bauman

Polytechnic Institute of Brooklyn

PRENTICE-HALL, INC., Englewood Cliffs, N.J.

To Katherine

FOUNDATIONS OF MODERN CHEMISTRY SERIES

Robert W. Parry and Henry Taube, Editors

Preface

The explosive growth of information in recent years has forced a re-evaluation of the content, timing, and sequential structure of courses at all levels of education. There is increasing recognition that, in attempting to "modernize" curricula, some difficult and complex subjects are being crammed into earlier courses without sufficient adaptation to the level of preparation of the students. However, it has also been shown that many topics previously considered very advanced and difficult are actually conceptually simple and independent of the subjects that have customarily preceded them. Many such topics can be taught very effectively much earlier in a student's career than has previously been attempted. Robert Hutchins pointed toward some of these desirable curriculum changes many years ago when he commented upon the incongruity of teaching such subtle and subjective subjects as history, civics, and geography to children, while leaving the comparatively straightforward, logical, and demonstrable physical sciences and mathematics to the later years.

Much of thermodynamics is so conceptually simple that it is now being taught considerably earlier than in the past. This is not to suggest that thermodynamics can be fully grasped in a first course, whenever it is offered; it is far too complex and subtle in many of its interconnections for that. It has, in fact, much in common with a field such as history. One does not learn history from a first course; rather it is necessary to acquire a familiarity with a few names, events, and dates to provide a framework into which other names, events, and dates are to be fit, sometimes loosely and sometimes snugly, until the puzzle begins to take shape and the emerging picture provides increased motivation for finding the missing parts. This has not prevented us from offering first courses in history.

Thermodynamics deals with many quantities already familiar to college students. From the beginning it provides connections between previously unrelated concepts and offers explanations for phenomena that have been directly observed by the students. It is much better suited to the freshman chemistry course than are many other topics presently included, for it requires very little reliance on formal physics or chemistry. Only a very rudimentary knowledge of calculus is needed, which can be satisfied by a concurrent course or by directed self-study. The goals of such an early introduction to thermodynamics should be: (1) to enable the student to work simple problems in areas such as thermochemistry, colligative properties, and chemical equilibrium, of the types customarily found in freshman chemistry courses; (2) to lead the student to a recognition that these equations and formulas are not mysterious, unrelated discoveries but are tied together by a broad, theoretical structure based on straightforward definitions and derivations that he can read and understand; and (3) to provide him with the necessary framework to which a later understanding of the foundations and implications of thermodynamics can be attached.

It is important to emphasize that the student being introduced to the subject at an early stage of his career is not expected to understand thermodynamics in either the breadth or depth appropriate for a more advanced course. For example, the subject of heat engines, though of immense practical, theoretical, and historical importance, can very well be omitted entirely, or left for the student to read on his own; and many of the convenient mathematical transformations can advantageously be put off until the student has become familiar with the thermodynamic functions as well as with the mathematical techniques required.

The simplicity and power of thermodynamics can be made apparent only when a fairly high degree of rigor is maintained, not in the sense of tightrope walking through exhaustive mathematical proofs but rather by considering the general case as far as possible, then looking for simplifications in special cases, with emphasis on the physical problem to which the general equations are to be applied. Otherwise the student may rapidly gain the impression that thermodynamics is rigorous only for nonexistent ideal gases and ideal solutions, and he may be unable to distinguish between derived and empirical results.

It is a pleasure to acknowledge the assistance of Professor James A. Goldman at many stages of the writing and revising of this book, the suggestions of Professors Richard Laity and Robert Parry, and the numerous helpful conversations on thermodynamics and related problems with Professor Ernest Loebl. The perseverance of my wife, who read the manuscript carefully and critically as one previously uninitiated into thermodynamics or calculus, has contributed in no small way to the removal of hidden assumptions and implicit or misplaced definitions.

The present form of the text is a revision of material presented during the spring of 1964 to the Advanced Placement Program chemistry class of the Bethpage (N.Y.) High School. I feel indebted to those students, as well as to the many college juniors who have over the past decade been the testing ground for methods of presentation of thermodynamics. Additional encouragement for the preparation of this volume has been provided by the students, both undergraduate and graduate, who have found the preliminary edition helpful, either as an introduction or as a review of thermodynamic principles.

Robert P. Bauman

Contents

An Introduction

to Thermodynamics

Thermodynamics deals with the flow of energy under conditions of equilibrium or near-equilibrium and with the associated properties of the equilibrium states of matter. It is a macroscopic theory, ignoring completely the details of atomic and molecular structure, though not the existence of atoms and molecules to the extent required for writing chemical reactions. Time is not recognized as a variable and cannot appear in thermodynamic equations. For students who have become familiar with atoms and molecules, it may be surprising to find how far one can go toward treating chemical and physical equilibria without employing any simplified models or delving into theories of molecular structure.

The detachment of thermodynamics from molecular theory is an important limitation, but it is an even more important asset. The fundamental principles of thermodynamics were developed during the 19th century, long before atomic structure was understood. Even today we need not worry about our vast ignorance at the molecular level, especially in the areas of liquids and ionic solutions, in applying thermodynamics to real systems. It has been said, with some justification, that if you can prove something by thermodynamics you need not do the experiment. Such a strong statement must be handled with care, but it should become clear in the following pages that common practice follows this assumption quite closely.

There is a companion to thermodynamics called statistical mechanics, or sometimes statistical thermodynamics or statistical physics, which starts with the time-dependent equations for molecular systems and reaches the equations of classical thermodynamics by finding time-average values. It can be shown that much the same basic postulates are required in statistical mechanics and classical thermodynamics, so that neither can be called more fundamental than the other. On the other hand, because many of the details of molecular interactions are incorporated into the theory, statistical mechanics requires much more complex mathematics. The rewards for this greater mathematical effort are a clearer picture of the molecular interactions, a check on the molecular theories on which the calculations are based, and a powerful means for pushing beyond the results of classical thermodynamics into the subject of nonequilibrium processes, in which rates are important. Space does not permit a discussion of statistical mechanics in this volume, but a few of the results from the theory are given where they will contribute significantly to the understanding or application of classical thermodynamics.

Before attacking the quantitative treatment of thermodynamics, it will be helpful to clarify the meaning of the thermodynamic term "heat." This can best be accomplished by consideration of a few qualitative or semi-quantitative experiments. For each of these we will develop a working hypothesis, select a crucial test, and revise the hypothesis as necessary.

Our understanding of heat is based upon common experiences. When we stand before a fire, or when we place a pan of water over a gas fire or in contact with an electrically heated coil, our senses and the change in character of the water tell us that something passes from the fire or hot coil to the surroundings (specifically, to us or to the pan of water). The effect is to "heat" the surrounding items, by which we mean that there is a sensation of warmth that can be verified by a thermometer. A thermometer, in some way, measures this "heat." We seek to find the relationship between temperature, heating, and heat.

As an initial hypothesis, assume that a thermometer measures the amount of heat. If so, we should find that a loss of temperature by one body is compensated by a gain of temperature by another. To test this we put 200 gm of hot water, at 90°C, into each of two Dewar flasks[1] (Figure 1). To the first flask we add 50 gm of water initially at 20°C, and stir until the temperature becomes steady. The new temperature is found to be about 76.0°C. To the second flask we add 25 gm of water, at 20°C, and find the final temperature to be about 82.2°C. We must ask now whether the experiment shows the initial hypothesis to be fully satisfactory or not. There has indeed been a loss of temperature by the water in the flask and a gain in temperature by the water added. But there is clearly no "temperature balance." The water in the flasks changed temperature only slightly,

---

[1]These are also called vacuum flasks, because the space between the double walls has been evacuated. Another common name for them is "Thermos" bottle, which is the trade name of the American Thermos Products Co.

whereas the water added increased in temperature several times as much. Also, the water in the second flask dropped in temperature less than that in the first flask, but the water added to the second flask increased in temperature more than that added to the first flask. Examination of the results (Table 1) shows that the drop in temperature of the water originally in the flasks is roughly doubled when twice as much cool water is added.

The experiment just described suggests how the original hypothesis must be revised. It appears that a larger amount of water can absorb more heat for a given temperature increase. The temperature, therefore, is more nearly a "concentration" of heat. From this revised hypothesis we can predict that the temperature change times the amount of the substance should be the same for both the added and the original water (see Table 1).

It is necessary to find out whether the same relationship will hold if we exchange

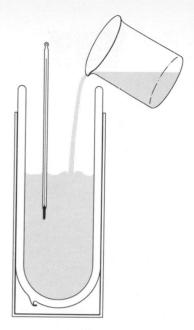

FIGURE 1 *Cool water (20° C) is added to hot water (90° C) in a Dewar flask that prevents passage of heat through the walls. Final temperatures are listed in Table 1.*

heat between two different substances. To do this we again prepare two flasks, each containing 200 gm of water at 90°C, then add to one a block of aluminum with a mass of 50 gm and to the second a block of aluminum with a mass of 25 gm (Figure 2). After a few seconds we find that the temperatures of the aluminum blocks are equal to the temperatures of the surrounding water—about 86.35°C for the larger block and 88.12°C for the smaller block. Multiplying temperature change by mass and comparing the result for the aluminum block and the water shows that the ratio is the same for both parts of the experiment with aluminum, but appreciably different from the results of the earlier experiment. We conclude, therefore, that aluminum and water have a different "heat capacity," so that a given amount of heat added to a certain mass of one produced a different temperature change than equal heat added to the same mass of the other.

We have left unanswered the question whether the "heat capacity" de-

Table 1 TEMPERATURE MEASUREMENTS*

Sample	T_{final}	ΔT_s	ΔT_w	$-\Delta T_w/\Delta T_s$	$-\Delta T_w M_w/\Delta T_s M_s$
H_2O, 50 gm	76.0	56.0	−14.0	0.25	1.0
H_2O, 25 gm	82.2	62.2	− 7.8	0.125	1.0
Al, 50 gm	86.35	66.35	− 3.65	0.0050	0.22
Al, 25 gm	88.12	68.12	− 1.88	0.0276	0.22

* Temperatures are in °C. Initial temperature of the water is 90°C and of the sample, 20°C. ΔT_s is the temperature change of the sample and ΔT_w is the temperature change of the water originally in the flask. M_s is the mass of the sample added and M_w the mass of water originally in the flask.

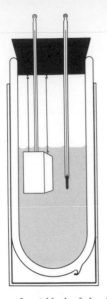

FIGURE 2 *A block of aluminum initially at 20° C is immersed in the water (at 90° C) and temperatures of the block and of the water are measured.*

pends upon the volume or the mass of the substance that is absorbing the heat. The choice can be easily made by means of an experiment employing a substance, such as air, that can readily change volume without changing mass. We fill one flask with air, evacuate a second identical flask, and immerse both in water, with a connection provided between the flasks, as shown in Figure 3. The temperature of the water is measured; then the stopcock is opened, allowing the air to expand to twice its initial volume, and the temperature of the water is remeasured. The temperature is found to be unchanged. From this we conclude that the temperature of the air did not change with the change in volume, and therefore that it is better to define the "heat capacity" in terms of mass rather than of volume.

In each of the measurements described thus far it has been possible to follow heat as it flows from one body to another; the amount lost by one substance has been equal to the amount gained by the other. It is necessary to determine whether this is always true. (If it is, we would say that heat is "conserved," or that the "amount of heat" is constant.) Taking a hint from the famous observations of Count Rumford, who noted the great quantities of heat evolved during the boring of cannons, we design our next experiment to include mechanical motion, in which work will be performed. Instead of expanding the air from one flask into an evacuated flask, we can let it expand against a piston, as shown in Figure 4. This time the temperature of the gas drops (about 50°C) during the expansion, even though we add insulation around the cylinder to prevent the flow of heat outward from the gas. The change of temperature cannot be solely because of the volume

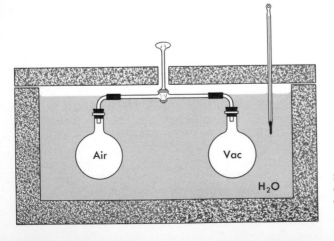

FIGURE 3 *When air expands into an evacuated container there is no significant change in temperature.*

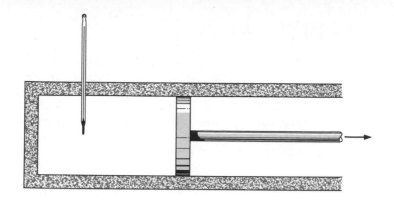

FIGURE 4 *When air expands slowly against a piston, the temperature drops.*

change; the previous experiment showed that the change of volume did not cause any change of temperature. The fact that the gas pushes on the piston, causing it to move, must be the important difference.

A few additional experiments will provide more information on the relationship between expansion, with work being done, and temperature effects on gases. (For brevity, only the results of these experiments will be discussed.) Compression of a gas causes an increase in the temperature just equal to the decrease of temperature during expansion, if both expansion and compression processes are slow. It is therefore possible, by repeated expansion and compression, to cycle the temperature between two values. Any other property of the gas that we might measure, such as density, volume, or viscosity, will be found to depend only on the temperature as measured by a thermometer, and not on how that temperature was achieved (for any specified pressure). In other words, the "heating effect" of a compression seems to be exactly the same as the heating effect of a flame or other source of heat. Thus it is possible to compress a gas, thereby raising its temperature; then extract heat from it by removing the insulation until the gas has returned to room temperature; expand it into an evacuated space without change of temperature; compress it to again increase its temperature; extract heat; and so forth, as many times as we wish.

Clearly, heat is not a quantity that retains its identity after it is absorbed by a substance, for we can add any amount of heat without changing the properties of a gas in any way (provided only that the proper amount of work is done by the gas). There is no property that will enable us to determine the amount of heat added to any substance, or the amount of heat removed. The description of temperature as the "concentration of heat" is therefore untenable, and must be abandoned. Temperature is related to a "concentration" of something more fundamental, which can give rise to heat or can cause a gas to do work and which is increased when the substance absorbs heat or when work is done on the substance. This quantity so directly related to temperature is called *energy*.[2]

---

[2]In a flowing liquid it may be necessary to distinguish between "internal energy," related to the temperature, and "total energy," which would include the kinetic energy associated with the movement of the liquid. Our concern is the former; we'll simply call it "energy."

The description of energy transfers as "heat" and "work" may be compared with deposits and withdrawals from a savings bank. The deposit slip may ask for a separate listing of bills and coins, and a withdrawal may be in the form of bills or coins. Yet the account balance itself is neither bills nor coins. In the same manner, energy may be put into a substance, or withdrawn from it, either as heat or as work, but it exists within the substance only as energy—not as heat or as work.

By going beyond thermodynamics, into statistical mechanics, the internal energy can be described in terms of kinetic energy and potential energy of individual atoms and molecules. But for purposes of thermodynamics we need know nothing more about energy than that it is related to the temperature and can be transferred to the surroundings either as heat or as work. We can find by experiments, such as the compression-cooling experiment or a variety of others performed by Joule, how much heat is equivalent to how much work and, for a given substance, how much heat or work must be put in for a given temperature rise. The relationships between temperature, energy, heat, and work will be considered quantitatively in the discussion of the first law of thermodynamics.

1

The First Law

of Thermodynamics

Thermodynamics is based on a small number of postulates, or assumptions. These are called the "laws"of thermodynamics because they are suggested by a great amount of accumulated experimental evidence. In fact it is extremely important to keep in mind that thermodynamics is important just because there is *total* agreement between the results of thermodynamics (properly applied) and all careful experimental results available to us. Since it is not possible to *prove* the fundamental assumptions of thermodynamics, both the postulates and the derived results of thermodynamics have often been challenged. In every showdown thus far, thermodynamics has been shown to be correct.

Energy

The best-known of the thermodynamic postulates, known as *the first law of thermodynamics,* is just the principle of the conservation of energy. This may be stated in the form: *The energy of the universe is constant.* A better form for our purposes is to write

$$(\Delta E)_{\text{system+surroundings}} = 0 \qquad (1)$$

The symbol Δ (Greek capital delta) indicates a *change* in the quantity that follows, in this instance a change in

7

the energy, E. Expressed in symbols,

$$\Delta E \equiv E_{final} - E_{initial} \tag{2}$$

In general, we are not interested in the problem of all the changes going on throughout the universe; rather, we are interested primarily in some small part of the universe, such as 50 gm of water, or 1 mole of H_2 gas, or 30 gm of $CuSO_4$ solution. This fixed quantity of substance[1] we will call the "system." Unless otherwise noted, a symbol such as ΔE will always refer to the system under discussion. When the energy of the system increases, ΔE is positive; when the energy of the system decreases, ΔE is negative. In any given problem the system to be considered must be carefully defined. The "surroundings" then includes the remainder of the universe or, perhaps more practically, enough of the universe so that the "process," or occurrence, under consideration will have no effect beyond the system and surroundings. It should be clear, therefore, that equation 1 is equivalent to the previous statement of the first law.

An important special case is the "isolated" system such as an insulated reaction vessel of constant volume. When the system is isolated, there are no changes in the surroundings produced by changes in the system. Thus it follows that the energy of an isolated system must be constant.

Systems that are not isolated can exchange energy with their surroundings in many ways: by mechanical collision, thermal conduction, radiation, electrical current through wires, static electromagnetic fields, or gravitational fields. It is convenient to divide all such energy *transfers* into two categories, which we shall call *heat* and *work*.

Heat must **not** be confused with thermal energy, which is that form of energy associated with the random motion of molecules within a substance. For any given substance the amount of thermal energy is measured by the temperature.[2] All substances contain thermal energy, but it is meaningless to speak of a substance "containing heat." Heat is a transfer of energy from one substance to another; heat is something that flows from a warmer body to a cooler body. For many years it was believed that substances did contain heat. Remnants of that older theory remain with us today in such terms as "latent heat," but in the 18th century this "caloric" theory of heat was shown to be incompatible with experimental observations. It may seem strange, at first, that one can get heat out of a glass of water if the water does not contain heat, but this is really no more strange than getting light, and heat, from a match when it is struck. We don't say that the match head contains "latent light"; we do say that the match head contains energy,

---

[1] In later work you may find it helpful to work with open systems, where the quantity of substance changes (as in a rocket that ejects combustion products), or with systems defined by a fixed volume (as in a hot-water heater with a cold-water inlet and hot-water outlet). For the present it is sufficient to consider only closed systems defined by the quantity of matter present.

[2] The higher the temperature, the more thermal energy is present. However, an increase of thermal energy need not raise the temperature if there is a change of phase, as in the boiling of water.

both thermal and chemical (potential), and this energy can escape as light or in other ways.

The division of the energy transfer into heat and work corresponds to a division into *random motion* and *directed motion*. At this point we have no good criterion for deciding whether light, for example, should be called "heat" or "work." Later we will find that the second law of thermodynamics deals with these distinctions. For the present we may consider the division to be quite arbitrary.

We could write the total energy change for the system in the form

$$\Delta E = (\Delta E)_{\text{heat}} + (\Delta E)_{\text{work}} \tag{3}$$

—but this is awkward. It is better, and conventional, to introduce new symbols for the terms on the right-hand side.

Let q be the amount of heat absorbed **by** the system from the surroundings. That is, if heat is absorbed by the system, q will be a positive quantity; if heat is lost by the system we may say that a negative amount of heat has been absorbed and q will be a negative quantity. $(\Delta E)_{\text{heat}} = q$. Let w be the amount of work done **by** the system. Work done by the system decreases the energy of the system, so $(\Delta E)_{\text{work}} = -w$. Thus

$$\Delta E = q - w \tag{4}$$

All energy transfers are measured either as heat or as work, or both. Furthermore, heat absorbed by the system is absorbed from the surroundings, and work done by the system is done on the surroundings. Thus equation 4 is the basis of the application of the first law of thermodynamics. It is called the *first-law equation*.[3] A few simple examples of energy changes, in the following sections, will show the meaning of the terms in equation 4.

TEMPERATURE CHANGES AND HEAT CAPACITY, C_V. Consider first the process of heating a gas confined in a container of constant volume. No work is done, since there is no directed motion.

$$(V) \qquad\qquad \Delta E = q \tag{5[4]}$$

The heat absorbed divided by the temperature rise is the quantity commonly called *heat capacity, C. C = q/\Delta T*. However, since C may itself vary with temperature, it is better to take the limiting value of the ratio for small changes of temperature. This is just a derivative.[5]

---

[3] Some authors prefer to let equation 4 serve as the statement of the first law. This can only be logically acceptable if q and w have been previously defined in such a way that there is no doubt that **all** energy changes are included in one term or the other. It should be noted also that the opposite sign convention is sometimes employed for work: $(\Delta E)_{\text{work}} = w$. Then $\Delta E = q + w$. This difference of convention cannot, of course, lead to physically different results.

[4] The notation (V) at the left of the equation indicates that the equation is valid when the volume of the system is held constant.

[5] See Appendix.

$$(V) \qquad \frac{dE}{dT} = \frac{\delta q}{dT} = C_V \qquad (6)$$

It should be noted, however, that whereas dT is an ordinary differential (that is, an infinitesimal **change** of the temperature, T), the numerator, δq, is not a change of any variable but is, rather, an infinitesimal **amount** of heat absorbed. Thus it is not proper to write dq (or Δq), and q/dT would not convey the precise meaning of the ratio of an *infinitesimal* amount of heat for an infinitesimal temperature change. The notation δq is one of the more common ways of meeting this problem (δ is the lower-case Greek letter, delta). Additional significance of the difference between dE or dT and δq (or δw) will be considered later.

It is common practice to represent a derivative, such as dE/dT, which is evaluated with some variable (in this case V) held constant, by the special symbol $\frac{\partial E}{\partial T}\big)_V$. These are called "partial derivatives." Employing this notation we arrive at the usual form of equation 6.

$$C_V = \frac{\partial E}{\partial T}\bigg)_V \qquad (6a)$$

Consider now the change in energy for 2 moles of H_2 warmed at constant volume from 25°C to 50°C. For hydrogen gas near room temperature, C_V is constant and is about 5 cal/mole-deg. The gas can do no work at constant volume so the total energy change is equal to the heat absorbed.

$$(V) \qquad dE = \frac{dE}{dT}\, dT = \frac{\partial E}{\partial T}\bigg)_V dT = C_V\, dT \qquad (7)$$

The total energy change is obtained by integration.

$$(V) \qquad \Delta E = E_2 - E_1 = \int_{T_1}^{T_2} dE \qquad (8)$$

$$= \int_{T_1}^{T_2} C_V\, dT = C_V(T_2 - T_1)$$

Thermodynamic temperatures are expressed on the Kelvin scale, by adding 273.15 to the temperature on the Celsius[6] scale. Temperature differences are the same for the two scales. With the appropriate numerical substitutions,

$$\Delta E = 2 \text{ moles} \times 5 \text{ cal/mole-deg} \times (323 - 298) \text{ deg}$$

$$= 250 \text{ cal}$$

This is the amount of heat that must be added to the gas to raise its temperature 25°C.

---

[6] This scale has commonly been called "centigrade" in English-speaking countries, a name that can be confused with $\frac{1}{100}$ degree in other languages.

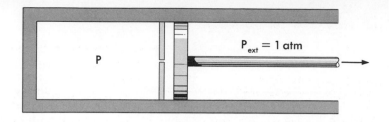

FIGURE 1 *An ideal gas, initially confined on the left under 3 atm pressure, expands through a pinhole and against the piston to a final pressure of 1 atm. Heat is supplied as necessary to maintain the temperature constant at 50° C.*

IDEAL-GAS EXPANSIONS.   Now let 2 moles of hydrogen, at 3 atm pressure, expand at a constant temperature of 50°C through a pinhole and against a piston. Assume the external pressure acting on the piston is 1 atm, as in Figure 1. The work done by the gas is the product of the force opposing the motion and the distance through which the piston moves. The force is $P_{ext}A$, where A is the area of the piston, and if dx is the distance moved, $A\, dx = dV$ is the change in volume.

(Effusion controlled) $w = \int f\, dx = \int P_{ext}A\, dx = \int P_{ext}\, dV$

Since P_{ext} is constant, it may be removed from the integral.

$$w = P_{ext} \int dV = P_{ext}\, \Delta V \qquad (9)$$

The initial and final volumes can be calculated from the ideal-gas[7] law, $PV = nRT$.

$$V_f = \frac{2 \text{ moles} \times 82.1 \text{ ml-atm/mole-deg} \times 323 \text{ deg}}{1 \text{ atm}}$$

$$V_i = \frac{2 \text{ moles} \times 82.1 \text{ ml-atm/mole-deg} \times 323 \text{ deg}}{3 \text{ atm}}$$

Thus the work is

$$w = P_{ext}\, \Delta V = P_{ext}(V_f - V_i)$$
$$= 1 \text{ atm } (53{,}000 - 17{,}700) \text{ ml} = 35{,}300 \text{ ml-atm}$$

It is often convenient to express the work in calories or in joules. The neces-

---

[7] The term "ideal" means simply that the substance obeys a certain equation. An ideal gas obeys the equation $PV = nRT$; in later chapters we will encounter the "ideal solution," which obeys an equation known as Raoult's law. The ideal-gas equation combines Boyle's law and Charles', or Gay-Lussac's, law into a single, more convenient expression. The temperature must be on an absolute scale, which we will always take as the Kelvin scale; n is the number of moles of gas; and R is a universal constant, whose value depends on the units chosen for pressure and volume. It should be noted that the product of pressure and volume has the dimensions of energy. Such gases as He, H_2, O_2, and N_2 closely follow the ideal-gas equation at room temperature; such easily condensable gases as CO_2 or H_2O vapor follow the equation much less closely.

THE FIRST LAW OF THERMODYNAMICS

Table 1 GAS CONSTANT
AND CONVERSION FACTORS

1 cal (defined) = 4.1840 joule = 41.3 ml-atm

1 ml-atm = 0.0242 cal = 0.1013 joule

1 joule = 0.239 cal = 9.89 ml-atm

$$R = \frac{1.987 \text{ cal}}{\text{mole-deg}} = \frac{8.314 \text{ joule}}{\text{mole-deg}} = \frac{82.06 \text{ ml-atm}}{\text{mole-deg}}$$

above, $w = 855$ cal $= 3580$ joule.

In order that the temperature may remain constant it is necessary to supply heat to the gas to compensate for the energy expended in doing work. From the first-law equation,

$$q = \Delta E + w$$

For the special case of an ideal gas, the energy depends only on the temperature, not on the pressure or volume. At constant temperature, therefore, $\Delta E = 0$ and the heat that must be supplied is

$$q = w = 855 \text{ cal}$$

A more important example than the expansion against a constant external pressure is the "reversible" and isothermal (constant temperature) expansion. A process is said to be thermodynamically reversible if it can be reversed at any stage by an infinitesimal increase in the opposing force or an infinitesimal decrease in the driving force. It should be clear that such a reversible process is an example of a limiting case, which is only approximately achieved in practice. Not only does it require a frictionless mechanism, but if the unbalance of forces is infinitesimal, the rate will be infinitesimal and the time required will be infinite. The question of reversibility will be considered in more detail later.

From the assumption that the operation is isothermal and the gas is ideal,

$$\Delta E = 0$$

and
$$q = w = \int P \, dV$$

Because the expansion is to be reversible, the pressure on the piston differs only infinitesimally from the equilibrium pressure of the gas, $P = nRT/V$. The work done by the gas is then

(*T*, I.G., rev) $\qquad w = \int nRT \, dV/V = nRT \ln(V_f/V_i)$ $\qquad\qquad$ (10)

For example, if 2 moles of hydrogen at 3 atm and 50°C is expanded isothermally and reversibly to a final pressure of 1 atm,

$$q = w = 2 \text{ moles} \times 1.987 \text{ cal/mole-deg} \times 323 \text{ deg} \times \ln V_f/V_i$$

Because the temperature is constant, $V_f/V_i = P_i/P_f = 3$.

$$q = w = 1283 \text{ cal} \ln 3 = 1410 \text{ cal}$$

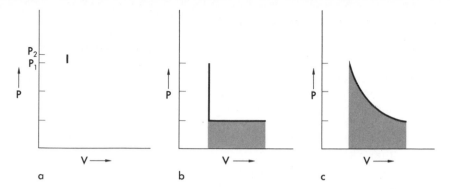

FIGURE 2 *Work performed by a gas when the pressure is changed. (a) If the pressure changes at constant volume, the work is the area under the vertical line, which is zero. (b) A discontinuity in pressure, followed by a constant pressure expansion, gives the work shown by the shaded area. (c) A reversible expansion gives the maximum possible work for the given temperature, as shown by the shaded area under the hyperbola.*

Notice that the work done, and the heat absorbed, is greater in the reversible expansion than in the previous case of expansion against a constant external pressure. A reversible expansion (or compression) must always give a maximum value for w.[8]

An integral may be represented by the area under a curve (see Appendix) and the three examples considered above may be compared graphically. When the gas was warmed, at constant volume, the pressure increased by the factor $T_f/T_i = 323/297 = 1.09$. In a plot of pressure against volume, this is represented by a vertical line (Figure 2a) and the area under such a line is zero. No work is performed.

The expansion against a constant opposing force is represented by the plot in Figure 2b. The gas, in escaping through the pinhole, changes its pressure from 3 atm to 1 atm, but there is a negligible change in volume associated with passage through the pinhole itself. When the gas is through the pinhole, however, it has the pressure of 1 atm and the volume increases, at this pressure, until all of the gas has reached the same pressure and occupies the total volume V_f. The work done is the area under the vertical

---

[8] A completely general proof that the reversible work is a maximum for the isothermal process cannot be given here, but this important result can be illustrated by considering the expansion or compression of a gas. When the piston moves *away from* the gas molecules the molecules do not strike the piston as hard as when the piston is stationary. The pressure exerted by the gas on the piston is therefore less than the pressure exerted by the gas on the stationary walls; the effective pressure is slightly less than the pressure of the gas. Therefore $\int P_{eff} \, dV < \int P \, dV$. The difference depends on the speed of the piston relative to the speeds of the gas molecules and disappears for sufficiently slow piston speeds. When the piston moves *toward* the gas molecules the molecules strike the piston harder and the effective pressure is greater than the equilibrium pressure, but the change in volume is negative. Therefore $\int P_{eff} \, dV$ is larger in magnitude than $\int P \, dV$, but since both are negative quantities, $\int P_{eff} \, dV < \int P \, dV$, as before. One often sees the expression $w = \int P_{ext} \, dV$ applied when P_{ext}, the external pressure, differs from the pressure of the system. Except in unusual circumstances this is not even a good approximation. See *J. Chem. Ed.* **41**, 102 and 674 (1964); **43**, 233 (1966).

line, which is zero, plus the area under the horizontal line, which is 1 atm times the volume change.

When the pressure of the gas changes smoothly, as in Figure 2c, the area under the curve is a maximum for the given temperature. The pressure follows the curve $PV =$ constant (where the constant is nRT), which is part of a hyperbola.

The condition to be satisfied in order that an expansion or compression of any fluid should be thermodynamically reversible, such that $w = \int P_{gas}\, dV$, is simply that the fluid have a well-defined, uniform pressure throughout. This must be true if there are no "leaks"—that is, no pinholes or porous membranes, such that the gas pressure is different on the two sides—and if the motion of the piston confining the gas is slow compared to the "relaxation time" of the fluid, or the time for pressures to equilibrate in the fluid. For a gas, this requires only that the expansion or compression must be very slow compared to the speed of sound in the gas. Unless there is such a well-defined pressure, or in certain situations (see Figure 1) two or more well-defined pressures, for the system, thermodynamics cannot be applied. It is then necessary to apply the more difficult methods of non-equilibrium, or irreversible, thermodynamics. That is, equilibrium thermodynamics is sufficient for reversible processes and certain types of irreversible processes; "irreversible thermodynamics" deals with the time-dependent equations that become necessary in other problems involving irreversible phenomena, such as diffusion rates and shock-wave propagation.

It is important to remember, however, that the existence of a well-defined "state" (an equilibrium state, for which pressure is defined) for the system does not ensure that the over-all process of expansion or compression will be reversible. Some of the work done by the gas may be done against frictional forces, or may be converted into kinetic energy of the piston and subsequently converted to thermal energy by collision of the piston with mechanical stops. Or there may be conduction of heat from the system to or from the surroundings at a lower or higher temperature. Thus the total process may consist of a sum of parts, some of which are reversible and some irreversible. It is particularly important in such circumstances to define carefully the system and surroundings and the exact process to be considered.

PHASE CHANGES.   Let 5 gm of ice melt at 0°C under 1 atm pressure. Experimental measurements have shown that the heat required, called the "heat of fusion," is 79.74 cal/gm. The work done is $\int P\, dV = 1$ atm $\times \Delta V$. The volumes of ice and water are 1.09 ml/gm and 1.00 ml/gm at 0°C. The energy change for the ice can be calculated from the first-law equation.

$$\Delta E = q - w = 5 \text{ gm} \times 79.74 \text{ cal/gm} - 1 \text{ atm}(1.00 - 1.09) \times 5 \text{ ml}$$

Conversion of the work term from ml-atm to cal gives

$$\Delta E = 398.70 + 0.01 \text{ cal} = 398.71 \text{ cal}$$

The total energy absorbed by the ice, ΔE, is slightly greater than the heat of fusion, q. The atmosphere does work on the system to make up the difference, although the amount of work done (0.01 cal) is negligible for nearly all purposes compared to the amount of heat absorbed (398.70 cal).

If 5 gm of water is vaporized at 100°C and 1 atm pressure, the energy change can be calculated in the same manner. The heat of vaporization is 539.7 cal/gm,[9] and for calculation of the work done it is sufficient to assume that the water vapor is an ideal gas.

$$\Delta E = q - w$$

$$= 539.7 \text{ cal/gm} \times 5 \text{ gm}$$

$$- 1 \text{ atm} \left(\frac{5}{18} \text{ mole} \times \frac{82.06 \text{ ml-atm/mole-deg}}{1 \text{ atm}} \times 373.15 \text{ deg} - 5 \text{ ml}\right)$$

$$= 2699 \text{ cal} - 8500 \text{ ml-atm}$$

$$= 2493 \text{ cal}$$

In problems of this type, however, an important shortcut is often satisfactory. The volume of the liquid is sufficiently small compared to that of the vapor that it may be neglected. Then the work term becomes

$$w = P(V_f - V_i) = PV_f = PnRT/P = nRT$$

The value of R in cal/mole-deg may be inserted into this expression to avoid completely the use of ml-atm and the conversion from ml-atm to cal. The entire problem can thus be written

$$\Delta E = q - w = 5 \text{ gm} \times 539.7 \text{ cal/gm} - \tfrac{5}{18} \text{ mole} \times 1.987 \text{ cal/mole-deg} \times 373 \text{ deg}$$

$$= 2493 \text{ cal}$$

CHEMICAL REACTIONS. An example of a gas-phase chemical reaction is the combustion of hydrogen at 100°C and 1 atm pressure (or slightly less) to give water vapor.

$$2 H_2 + O_2 \longrightarrow 2 H_2O$$

The heat of reaction (the heat absorbed) is $-57,960$ cal/mole(H_2O). That is, a negative amount of heat is absorbed by the reacting system, or a positive amount of heat is given up by the reacting system to the surroundings. The work done by the system is

$$w = \int P \, dV = P(V_f - V_i) = P(n_f RT/P - n_i RT/P) = (n_f - n_i)RT$$

$$w = (\Delta n)RT \tag{11}$$

---

[9] This heat of vaporization is required to separate the molecules from each other—that is, it represents an increase in the potential energy of the molecules. The kinetic energy is practically unchanged.

and the energy change of the reacting system is

$\Delta E = q - w$

$\quad = 2 \text{ moles}(-57{,}960 \text{ cal/mole}) - (-1 \text{ mole}) \times 1.987 \text{ cal/mole-deg} \times 373 \text{ deg}$

$\quad = -115{,}170 \text{ cal}$

The same reaction, at 100°C and 1 atm pressure (or slightly more) but producing liquid water rather than water vapor, will have a heat of reaction that differs from that of the preceding problem by the heat of vaporization of water.

$q = -115{,}920 \text{ cal} - 2 \text{ moles} \times 18 \text{ gm/mole} \times 539.7 \text{ cal/gm}$

$\quad = -135{,}350 \text{ cal}/(2 \text{ moles } H_2O)$

The work differs also, because ΔV is different. Neglecting the volume of the liquid, $\Delta V = (\Delta n)RT/P = (-3)RT/P$.

$w = P\,\Delta V = -3\,RT = -3 \times 1.987 \times 373 \text{ cal} = -2238 \text{ cal}$

Then the energy change of the system is

$\Delta E = q - w = -135{,}350 + 2238 \text{ cal}$

$\quad = -133{,}110 \text{ cal}$

Enthalpy

Chemical reactions and phase changes are more often carried out at constant pressure than at constant volume. At constant volume (no work done) the energy change is equal to the heat absorbed, but under constant pressure a correction must be made for the work performed against this pressure. Consider a completely general constant-pressure process in which the only work done is because of the volume change.

(P) $\qquad\qquad \Delta E = q - w = q - P(V_2 - V_1)$

which can be written

$$\Delta E = q - (P_2V_2 - P_1V_1)$$

where $P_1 = P_2$. Set $\Delta E = E_2 - E_1$ and rearrange.

$$q = E_2 - E_1 + P_2V_2 - P_1V_1$$
$$\quad = E_2 + P_2V_2 - (E_1 + P_1V_1)$$

or

(P) $\qquad\qquad\qquad q = \Delta(E + PV)$ $\qquad\qquad$ (12)

This last equation will be encountered so often that it is a great convenience to introduce a new symbol for the quantity $E + PV$.

$$H \equiv E + PV \tag{13}$$

Then if pressure is constant and the only form of work is $\int P \, dV$,

$$(P) \qquad\qquad\qquad \Delta H = q \tag{14}$$

The function H is called the "enthalpy."

Note that the enthalpy has now been defined by equation 13, which requires no assumptions of constant pressure, temperature, or volume. The enthalpy will, however, be found to be most convenient for problems in which pressure is constant.

A comparison between energy and enthalpy, E and H, can be made by calculating the enthalpy changes for the same processes for which energy changes were previously found.

TEMPERATURE CHANGES AND HEAT CAPACITY, C_P.　We found that for 2 moles of H_2 warmed at constant volume from 25°C to 50°C, $\Delta E = 250$ cal. For the same process, the enthalpy change is

$$\Delta H = \Delta(E + PV) = \Delta E + \Delta(PV) = \Delta E + V\Delta P$$
$$= \Delta E + V(nRT_f/V - nRT_i/V) = \Delta E + nR\Delta T$$
$$= \Delta E + 2 \text{ moles} \times 2 \text{ cal/mole-deg} \times 25 \text{ deg}$$
$$= 350 \text{ cal}$$

The enthalpy change is greater than the energy change because the increase in temperature causes an increase in P and thus in the product PV.

If the gas is warmed at constant pressure, rather than at constant volume, the enthalpy change can be calculated in much the same way.

$$\Delta H = \Delta E + \Delta(PV) = \Delta E + P\Delta V = \Delta E + nR\,\Delta T$$
$$= 350 \text{ cal}$$

The enthalpy, like the energy, depends only on the temperature, for an ideal gas. It is for this reason that we find the same ΔH (as well as the same ΔE) when the hydrogen gas is warmed by 25°C whether the process is at constant volume or constant pressure, or under other conditions.

It should be observed that in the constant-pressure process the correction term to obtain the enthalpy change from the energy change is a work term, $P\Delta V$. But in the constant-volume process the correction term is of equal magnitude and is not a work term, having instead the form $V\Delta P$.

The constant-pressure warming process can be treated in a somewhat different manner. Employing equation 14, since the pressure is constant,

$$(P) \qquad\qquad\qquad dH = \delta q$$

THE FIRST LAW OF THERMODYNAMICS

(P)
$$\frac{dH}{dT} = \frac{\delta q}{dT}$$

or
$$\left.\frac{\partial H}{\partial T}\right)_P = C_P \tag{15}$$

For H_2 gas near room temperature, C_P is about 7 cal/mole-deg. Inserting this value,

$$\Delta H = \int \left(\frac{\partial H}{\partial T}\right)_P dT = \int C_P \, dT$$

$$= 2 \text{ moles} \times 7 \text{ cal/mole-deg} \times 25 \text{ deg}$$

$$= 350 \text{ cal}$$

The heat capacity at constant pressure, C_P, is greater than, or occasionally equal to, the heat capacity at constant volume, C_V. The difference is small for solids and liquids, but for an ideal gas the difference is appreciable and is easily calculated. The constant-pressure and constant-volume restrictions can be dropped from the derivatives of equations 6a and 15 for the special case of an ideal gas, because both the energy and enthalpy of an ideal gas are independent of pressure and volume. Taking 1 mole of gas,

$$C_P = \frac{dH}{dT} = \frac{dE}{dT} + \frac{d(PV)}{dT} = \frac{dE}{dT} + \frac{d(RT)}{dT}$$

and therefore, setting $\frac{dH}{dT} = C_P$ and $\frac{dE}{dT} = C_V$, and noting that $\frac{d(RT)}{dT} = R\frac{dT}{dT} = R$, we obtain

(I.G.)
$$C_P = C_V + R \tag{16}$$

IDEAL-GAS EXPANSIONS.   The work performed by an ideal gas in an isothermal expansion was calculated previously for two important special cases (equations 9 and 10). Since the energy of an ideal gas is independent of pressure and volume, the energy change in an isothermal expansion is zero. The heat absorbed is therefore equal to the work done. At constant temperature the product PV is constant for an ideal gas, so the enthalpy change is equal to the energy change; that is, the enthalpy change is also zero for any isothermal expansion of an ideal gas.

PHASE CHANGES.   The "heat of fusion" is the heat absorbed by a solid when it melts under constant pressure. From equation 14 this is identically ΔH for the fusion process. Similarly, the "heat of vaporization" is ΔH_{vap}. Although ΔE_{fusion} is practically identical with ΔH_{fusion} because of the small volume changes involved, the difference between ΔE_{vap} and ΔH_{vap} can be appreciable, as was shown above. Tabulated values are invariably the enthalpy changes.

CHEMICAL REACTIONS.   The "heat of reaction," as tabulated, assumes constant pressure and is therefore identical with the ΔH of reaction.[10] This means that the partial pressure of any gaseous reactant or product is the same (usually 1 atm) before and after the reaction occurs. Thus both the individual partial pressures and the total pressure are constant.

It should be noted in particular that a chemical reaction, as interpreted for purposes of thermodynamics, does not mean that one starts with reactants, in the absence of products, and ends with products, in the absence of reactants. Rather, the process considered is a mixture of reactants and products, each at a fixed concentration or pressure, in which some reactants combine to give some products without change of temperature, pressure, or concentrations. One way of achieving this experimentally would be to have the total amount of material large, and allow only a small part of the reactants to combine. (A great advantage of electrochemistry for thermodynamic measurements, as discussed in Chapter 4, is the ease of carrying out reactions under these conditions.) The distinction between such a reaction at fixed concentrations and a reaction in which concentrations change is often unimportant for measurements of the enthalpy of reaction, but it will be very important in subsequent considerations of reacting systems (e.g., p. 73).

State Functions

Those properties—such as energy, enthalpy, temperature, pressure, and volume—that depend on the state of a system are called *state functions*. An important question is how much information we must have about any system in order to determine its state, and hence to fix completely its physical and chemical properties. If measurements carried out in Boston, Brooklyn, and Berkeley are to be compared, it is necessary that each person be sure he is working with a system that is substantially identical with those of his colleagues.

EXTENSIVE AND INTENSIVE PROPERTIES.   Where necessary, the amount of the system must be specified. Some properties, such as energy, heat capacity (C_P or C_V), or volume will be proportional to the amount of material taken. These are called "extensive" properties. Other quantities, such as pressure, temperature, and density, are independent of the amount of material and are called "intensive" properties. Extensive properties are commonly expressed "per mole," "per gram," or on a similar basis; the molar volume (that is, volume per mole), density, and molar heat capacities are examples of intensive properties derived from extensive properties.

Apart from the size of the system, the most obvious variable to control is the composition. For a "pure" substance, the degree of purity and the nature of the residual impurities should be known. For a solution, the

---

[10] Occasionally the term "heat of reaction" will refer to the heat given off; in this case it will be $-\Delta H_{reaction}$. The best check is to look for a known exothermic reaction, such as hydrogen plus oxygen to give water, to see whether ΔH is given (negative value) or $-\Delta H$ (positive value).

concentration of each of the components is required. Where there are possible differences of phase (solid, liquid, or vapor, or more than one crystal structure) the phase studied must be reported. In addition, each worker must be able to reproduce exactly such properties of the system as temperature, pressure, volume, density, viscosity, and refractive index.

Fortunately, if each system can be assumed to be at equilibrium (in its most stable state), not all of these variables are required. If the composition and mass are known, it is in general necessary to know only two additional variables. For example, if the temperature and pressure are known the volume can be calculated (assuming the necessary measurements have been previously made) whether the substance is solid, liquid, or gaseous; and from this the density, viscosity, and refractive index follow. To define the state of a gas it would be equally satisfactory to specify the pressure and volume, or the volume and temperature. On the other hand, knowing that 1 gm of water has a volume of 1.000132 ml under 1 atm pressure does not determine whether the temperature is 0°C or 8.1°C, because the water has a minimum volume, or maximum density, at 4°C. Nor could one determine the pressure accurately if given the volume and temperature of a liquid or solid. This demonstrates that some discretion is required when variables other than pressure and temperature are selected.

EXACT DIFFERENTIALS AND LINE INTEGRALS. A property, or state function, can depend only on the present state of a system. It cannot depend on history—that is, on how the system arrived at that state—provided we limit the discussion to equilibrium states, so that there can be no strains in solids, or other residual effects. It follows, therefore, that the change in such an equilibrium property, in going from one state to another, can depend only on the initial and final states. Mathematically this means that the change, described by an integral, depends only on the limits of the integral. For example,

$$\Delta E = E_2 - E_1 = \int_{E_1}^{E_2} dE$$

Nothing need be known about the process except the energy of the initial state, E_1, and the energy of the final state, E_2, to find ΔE. Integrands of this type are called *exact differentials*.

Most integrals are well defined in themselves. For example,

$$\int_{x_1}^{x_2} x\, dx = \tfrac{1}{2}x_2^2 - \tfrac{1}{2}x_1^2$$

$$\int_{x_1,y_1}^{x_2,y_2} (x\, dy + y\, dx) = x_2 y_2 - x_1 y_1$$

Some, however, are not defined. For example,

$$\int_{x_1,y_1}^{x_2,y_2} y\, dx$$

cannot be evaluated without additional information. If y is known as a function of x, then we can make a plot of y vs. x, as in Figure 3. Then, for example, if $y = x^2 + 3$,

$$\int_{x_1, y_1}^{x_2, y_2} y \, dx = \int_{x_1}^{x_2} (x^2 + 3) \, dx = \tfrac{1}{3}x_2^3 + 3x_2 - (\tfrac{1}{3}x_1^3 + 3x_1)$$

We can say that $\int y \, dx$ has been integrated along the line shown in Figure 3. This is called a *line integral*.[11]

Line integrals appear in thermodynamics when it is necessary to evaluate a quantity that depends on the path. Letting $y = P$ and $x = V$ in the example above gives the familiar integral for work,

$$w = \int P \, dV$$

It is not sufficient to know initial and final states (the end points of the line); the exact path must be known. This was demonstrated for the calculation of work in Figure 2. Heat absorbed by a system also depends on the path, so q is given by a line integral.

EQUATIONS OF STATE. Knowledge of two properties, or state functions, is generally sufficient to know, in principle, all other state functions. For example, if the pressure and temperature of n moles of an ideal gas are known, the volume can be found from the "equation of state," $V = nRT/P$, or $PV = nRT$. Any substance, whether an ideal gas or not, follows an equation of state relating the pressure, volume, and temperature; but the true equation of state may be a very complicated function and, indeed, may not be known accurately. Several functions have been proposed as good approximations to the equations of state for real gases. The best-known is that suggested by van der Waals:

$$(P + n^2a/V^2)(V - nb) = nRT$$

In this equation, a and b are constants that depend on the particular gas to be described. When the volume is large and at high temperatures, the terms involving a and b are negligible and the gas behaves as an ideal gas; but as the gas is cooled and/or compressed, the behavior deviates more and more from the ideal-gas law, until eventually the gas condenses to a liquid or solid.

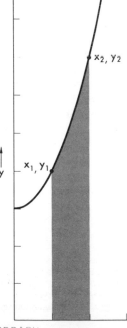

FIGURE 3 *The integral, $\int y \, dx$, represented by the area under the curve, depends not only on the initial and final points but also on the particular path, or line, followed between the points.*

---

[11] For a more thorough treatment of exact differentials and line integrals see advanced calculus books. There is a direct mathematical test to determine whether or not a function of two variables is an exact differential.

It should also be possible to relate the volume of any liquid or solid to its temperature and pressure, or to express such other properties as refractive index, heat capacity at constant volume or pressure, thermal conductivity, heats of vaporization or fusion, or vapor pressures of solids or liquids, in terms of the temperature and pressure. Some of these equations will be encountered in later chapters.

Thermochemistry

The application to chemical reactions of the principles developed thus far is called *thermochemistry*. In particular, the heats of reaction are measured and tabulated, and from these and from measured specific heats the enthalpy changes are calculated for other reactions or for other experimental conditions.

HESS'S LAW.   The enthalpy change for a chemical reaction, such as the oxidation of sulfur dioxide to sulfur trioxide—

$$2\ SO_2(g) + O_2 \longrightarrow 2\ SO_3(liq)$$

—can be expressed as the difference between the enthalpies of the initial and final states.

$$\Delta H_{reaction} = H_{final} - H_{initial}$$
$$= H(2\ SO_3) - H(2\ SO_2) - H(O_2)$$

There is no way within thermodynamics of measuring an absolute energy,[12] or an absolute enthalpy. Only energy, and enthalpy, changes can be determined. However, since these energy and enthalpy changes depend only on the initial and final states, it is possible to add and subtract chemical reactions and add and subtract the corresponding enthalpy changes. In particular, it is possible to tabulate "heats of formation," the enthalpy changes in the reaction of the elements to form each compound, and from these to calculate enthalpies of other reactions. This principle is known as *Hess's law*.

The reactions for the formation of the gases SO_2 and SO_3 are

$$S + O_2 \longrightarrow SO_2$$
$$S + \tfrac{3}{2} O_2 \longrightarrow SO_3$$

and the measured enthalpy changes for these reactions at 25°C and 1 atm pressure are $-70,960$ and $-104,670$ cal/mole. Subtraction of the first reaction from the second gives

$$SO_2 + \tfrac{1}{2} O_2 \longrightarrow SO_3$$

---

[12] The absolute energy of any system is simply the mass of the system times the square of the speed of light in vacuum, according to the special theory of relativity. However, it would be necessary to measure masses about a million times more accurately than is now possible if we were to determine energies to the accuracy required in thermochemistry.

and subtraction of the enthalpy changes gives $-33,710$ cal/mole, which is the heat of reaction for the oxidation of SO_2 to SO_3.

Exactly the same elements, in the same quantities, always appear on both sides of a chemical equation. Subtraction of the elements from both sides of an equation will yield, on each side, product minus reactants for the reactions of formation of each of the substances appearing in the original equation. In the example above, the original equation was $SO_2 + \frac{1}{2}O_2 \longrightarrow SO_3$. Subtract one mole of S and $\frac{3}{2}$ mole of O_2 from each side. The equation can then be written

$$(SO_2 - S - O_2) + (\tfrac{1}{2}O_2 - \tfrac{1}{2}O_2) \longrightarrow (SO_3 - S - \tfrac{3}{2}O_2)$$

and therefore

$$\Delta H_{\text{reaction}} = \Delta H_{\text{form}}(SO_3) - \Delta H_{\text{form}}(SO_2 - \Delta H_{\text{form}}(\tfrac{1}{2}O_2)$$
$$= -104,670 - (-70,960) - 0$$
$$= -33,710 \text{ cal/mole}(SO_3)$$

An entirely equivalent way of obtaining the same numbers is to consider the enthalpy of each compound on a scale taken with reference to the elements. Such enthalpy values are called *standard enthalpies* of the compounds; they are identical with the *standard enthalpies of formation.*

Hess's law can often be applied to find heats of reaction that could not be directly measured experimentally. For example, the reaction of two molecules of ethylene, C_2H_4, to form cyclobutane, C_4H_8, would not readily occur quantitatively under conditions conducive to measurement of the heat of reaction. But both ethylene and cyclobutane can be burned in oxygen, and subtraction of these reactions can give the reaction equation desired:

$$2\,C_2H_4 + 8\,O_2 \longrightarrow 4\,CO_2 + 4\,H_2O$$
$$C_4H_8 + 8\,O_2 \longrightarrow 4\,CO_2 + 4\,H_2O$$

Subtraction of the second from the first gives

$$2\,C_2H_4 \longrightarrow C_4H_8$$

and, therefore, subtraction of the ΔH for the second combustion from the ΔH for the first combustion gives ΔH for the condensation reaction. Heats of combustion[13] are comparatively easy to measure and are often tabulated.

KIRCHHOFF'S LAW. The heat of reaction at a temperature other than that given in a table can be found by calculating enthalpy changes along an arbitrary path. The total enthalpy change is independent of this choice of path. The method is known as *Kirchhoff's law.*

---

[13] The term "heat of combustion" usually means the heat given off, and is therefore $-\Delta H_{\text{combustion}}$.

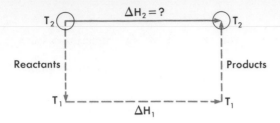

FIGURE 4 *The dotted path gives the same ΔH as does the reaction at the temperature T_2.*

Assume that ΔH is known for a reaction at a temperature T_1 and the ΔH at another temperature, T_2, is to be found. Starting with the hot reactants at T_2 (Figure 4), the reaction could be carried out isothermally to obtain products at the same temperature. An alternative path would be to cool the reactants to the temperature T_1, carry out the reaction isothermally at T_1, and warm the products to T_2. The heat of reaction at T_1 is already known and if the heat capacities at constant pressure are known the enthalpy changes can be calculated for the processes of cooling reactants and warming products. This path must give the same ΔH as the isothermal reaction at T_2.

$$\Delta H_2 = \int_{T_2}^{T_1} C_P(\text{reactants})\, dT + \Delta H_1 + \int_{T_1}^{T_2} C_P(\text{products})\, dT \qquad (17)$$

or, because interchanging limits of an integral will change the sign,

$$\Delta H_2 = \Delta H_1 + \int_{T_1}^{T_2} [C_P(\text{products}) - C_P(\text{reactants})]\, dT$$

If the difference in heat capacities is independent of temperature, this may be rewritten in the form

$$\Delta H_2 = \Delta H_1 + [C_P(\text{products}) - C_P(\text{reactants})](T_2 - T_1) \qquad (18)$$

For example, given that the heat of reaction for rhombic sulfur burning in oxygen to yield sulfur dioxide gas is $-70{,}960$ cal/mole at $25°C$ ($298°K$), find ΔH at $95°C$ ($368°K$). The heat capacities are given in Table 2. Insertion of the numerical values into equation 18 gives

$$\Delta H_{368} = -70{,}960 + (10.0 - 6.97 - 5.67) \times 70$$
$$= -71{,}140 \text{ cal/mole}$$

Table 2 HEAT CAPACITIES
Average values (in cal/mole-deg) for temperature ranges indicated

Compound	C_P	Temperature, $°C$
He	5.0	-200 up
H_2	6.95	25 to 200
O_2	6.97	25 to 200
H_2O (g)	8.7*	25 to 200
SO_2 (g)	10.0	25 to 120
S (r)	5.67	25 to 100
S (m)	6.18	95 to 120

* For rough calculations it is sufficient to set $C_P(\text{steam}) = C_P(\text{ice}) = \frac{1}{2}C_P(\text{liq } H_2O)$.

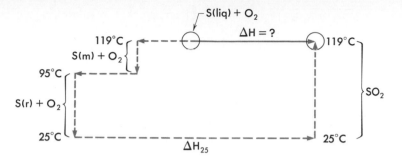

FIGURE 5   *To find $\Delta H_{reaction}$ at $119°C$, one may follow an alternate path. Freeze the liquid sulfur to monoclinic sulfur, cool this to $95°C$, convert the monoclinic sulfur to rhombic sulfur, cool the rhombic sulfur to $25°C$, react the sulfur with oxygen (also cooled from $119°C$), and warm the SO_2 product to $119°C$.*

Sometimes there will be a phase transition during the warming or cooling process. Sulfur has a phase change at 95°C, at which point rhombic sulfur goes to monoclinic sulfur; the monoclinic sulfur melts at 119°C. The enthalpy changes are 2816 and 9376 cal/mole. The heat of reaction for liquid sulfur burning in oxygen to form SO_2 at 119°C (392°K) can be calculated as follows (see Figure 5).

$$\Delta H_{392} = -\Delta H_{fusion} - C_P(m)(119 - 95) - \Delta H_{tr}$$
$$- C_P(r)(95 - 25) - C_P(O_2)(119 - 25)$$
$$+ \Delta H_{298} + C_P(SO_2)(119 - 25)$$
$$\Delta H_{392} = -9376 - 6.18 \times 24 - 2816 - 5.67 \times 70$$
$$- 6.97 \times 94 - 70{,}960 + 10.0 \times 94$$
$$= -83{,}410 \text{ cal/mole}$$

Note that temperature *differences* can be found without conversion to the Kelvin scale.

Both Hess's law and Kirchhoff's law are simply applications of the principle that changes in a state function, such as the enthalpy, are completely determined by the initial and final states. This principle is combined with the equation arising from the first law that shows that **if** the pressure is constant, the enthalpy change will be equal to the heat absorbed by the system. Thus the "heat of reaction," by which we mean $\Delta H_{reaction}$ (at a particular temperature, pressure, and concentrations of reactants and products), is only equal to the heat absorbed **if** the reaction proceeds at constant pressure (and at the specified temperature and concentrations). It is sometimes more convenient to carry out a reaction at constant volume. Then the heat absorbed is not equal to the "heat of reaction" (that is, to $\Delta H_{reaction}$), but it is still determinate because heat absorbed equals the change in energy when the system follows a constant-volume path and because $\Delta E_{reaction}$ is fixed by the initial and final states.

The experimental determination of a heat of reaction is called *calorimetry*. A typical calorimeter (Figure 6) consists of a reaction chamber, surrounded by a layer of water, enclosed by sufficient insulation to prevent heat loss to the surrounding laboratory. The reactants, at room temperature, are placed in the reaction chamber, the calorimeter is closed, and the

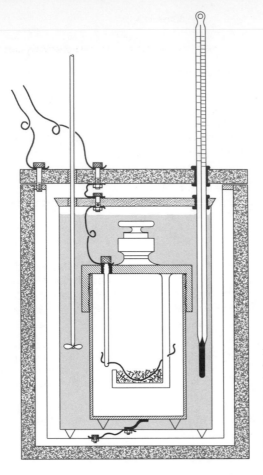

FIGURE 6 *Schematic representation of a bomb calorimeter. The sample and ignition wire are placed in the steel bomb, which is then closed, filled with oxygen under pressure, and covered with a known quantity of water. The wire is heated electrically to ignite the sample and the temperature rise of the water is measured.*

reaction is initiated by an electrically heated wire or other controlled energy source. The reaction will normally be exothermic and the reaction chamber will therefore become quite hot, but the heat is conducted into the surrounding water layer so that the products, and the water, reach a final temperature only slightly above the initial temperature. The $\Delta E_{\text{reaction}}$ is the same as if the entire process had occurred at the initial temperature, even though the materials may have become quite hot during the course of the reaction. The heat given off by the reaction is calculated by observing the temperature rise of the water, using the condition that all heat given off by the reaction must have been absorbed by the water. Small corrections are required for the change of temperature, from the initial room temperature, of the products, and for the small amount of energy added by the hot wire or other initiation method. Some systems may also require a correction for the changes of concentrations during the reaction.

Problems

1. The heat capacity (C_V) of most solid elements (except the very light ones) is about 6 cal/mole-deg around 298°K. Specific heat is the heat capacity per gram per degree. (For solids the difference between constant volume and constant pressure conditions is very small and may be neglected here.)

    a. Find the specific heat of Pb (in cal/gm-°C).

    b. Find the specific heat of Cu.

    c. Find ΔE for 25 gm of Cu when it is warmed from 20°C to 35°C.

2. Estimate the final temperature when 10 cm³ of iron (density 7.86 gm/ml) at 80°C is added to 30 ml of water at 20°C.

3. Three moles of N_2 gas at 4 atm pressure expands slowly at 25°C against a constant pressure of 1 atm. Find the work done

    a. in ml-atm

    b. in cal

    c. in joules

Compare with the work done by the gas if the expansion is reversible (and isothermal). What is ΔE for the gas in each process?

4. Calculate the work done when one-fourth mole of SO_2 at 27°C and 1 atm expands reversibly and isothermally to a final pressure of one-fifth atm. Find q for the gas during this process.

5. Calculate the final temperature if an ice cube weighing 25 gm, at −5°C, is added to a cup of coffee (150 ml, or "⅔ cup") at 90°C, neglecting heat loss to the surroundings.

6. The heat of vaporization of benzene, C_6H_6, is 7353 cal/mole and the normal boiling point is 80.1°C.

    a. What is ΔE_{vap} if the vapor is an ideal gas?

    b. Part of the heat absorbed by a liquid as it vaporizes to a gas is required to perform work on the atmosphere as the substance expands to a vapor. What fraction of the total heat absorbed goes into work against the atmosphere when benzene (density about 0.88 gm/ml) vaporizes at its normal boiling point?

7. Find ΔE at 25°C for the oxidation of S(rhombic) to give SO_2(gas) and for the oxidation of S to give SO_3(liq). The heats of reaction are −70,960 and −104,670 cal/mole. Assume gases are ideal.

8. Calculate ΔH and ΔE for the reaction, at 25°C,

$$SO_2(g) + \tfrac{1}{2} O_2 \longrightarrow SO_3(g)$$

The heat of vaporization of SO_3 at 25°C is 127.6 cal/gm.

9. Manganese can be prepared by a thermite process,

$$3\ Mn_3O_4 + 8\ Al \longrightarrow 9\ Mn + 4\ Al_2O_3$$

The standard enthalpy of formation of Mn_3O_4 is −331,400 cal/mole and for Al_2O_3, −400,400 cal/mole. Find the amount of heat given off by the reaction as written above, starting with the reactants at room temperature and ending with the products at room temperature.

10. The interconversion of graphite and diamond does not occur at room temperature. Explain how you could determine ΔH for this transition by measurements in the laboratory.

11. Calculate the heat of vaporization of water at 50°C.

12. Find ΔH for the hydrogenation of ethylene to produce ethane,

$$C_2H_4 + H_2 \longrightarrow C_2H_6$$

at 150°C. The standard heats of formation, at 25°C, of ethylene and ethane are 12,496 and −20,236 cal/mole, respectively. Average heat capacities (C_P) of ethylene, hydrogen, and ethane over this temperature interval are 11.98, 6.94, and 14.54 cal/mole-deg. All three compounds are gases at room temperature and above.

13. Benzene, C_6H_6, is reduced commercially with hydrogen to give cyclohexane, C_6H_{12}.

$$C_6H_6 + 3\,H_2 \longrightarrow C_6H_{12}$$

At room temperature (25°C) the benzene and cyclohexane are liquids and the heat of reaction is $-49,250$ cal/mole. Benzene boils at 80.1°C with a heat of vaporization of 94 cal/gm; cyclohexane boils at 80.7°C with a heat of vaporization of 86 cal/gm. The average heat capacity of liquid benzene is 0.44 cal/gm-deg, of liquid cyclohexane 0.41 cal/gm-deg, of benzene vapor 26.7 cal/mole-deg, of cyclohexane vapor 35.8 cal/mole-deg, and of H_2 6.94 cal/mole-deg. Find ΔH for the reduction of benzene with hydrogen at 150°C.

14. Air is approximately 20% O_2 and 80% N_2, by volume. Find the effective "molecular weight" of air. Calculate the density of air at 25°C and 1 atm, in gm/L, assuming it acts as an ideal gas.

15. A gaseous compound, containing only sulfur and fluorine, contains 62.7% (by weight) of sulfur. At 27°C and 750 torr[14] the density of the gas is 4.09 gm/L. What is the molecular formula of the compound? Assume the gas is ideal.

16. Find the pressure exerted by 32 gm of methane in a 2 L steel bomb at 127°C assuming the gas is ideal.

17. Find the pressure exerted by 32 gm of methane in a 2 L steel bomb at 127°C assuming the gas obeys van der Waals' equation. The constants may be taken as $a = 2.25$ L^2atm/mole^2 and $b = 0.0428$ L/mole.

18. Find the volume occupied by 32 gm of methane at a pressure of 5 atm at 27°C if the gas is ideal. Use this value to calculate the n^2a/V^2 correction term in the van der Waals equation and find, from this, an approximate value for the volume occupied by the methane if it obeys van der Waals' equation. Recalculate the correction term, using this better volume, and recalculate the volume, if necessary.

19. A good vacuum obtained with a mechanical pump and a mercury diffusion pump will measure 10^{-5} torr, or better, of "noncondensable" gases (such as air), but there is 10^{-3} torr of mercury vapor present unless this has been trapped out. Exceptionally good vacuum systems can give 10^{-9} torr.
  a. How many molecules/cc are there at a pressure of 10^{-3} torr?
  b. How many molecules/cc are there at a pressure of 10^{-9} torr?
  c. What pressure would be required to achieve 1 molecule/cc?

---

[14] The *torr* is a unit of pressure equal to $\frac{1}{760}$ of the standard atmosphere. It is numerically equivalent to the unit "mm of Hg" but is less awkward, especially when mercury is one of several vapors present. The torr is named after Evangelista Torricelli, who invented the barometer in the 17th century.

2

The Second Law

of Thermodynamics

During the 19th century several men, of quite different backgrounds and interests, struggled with the basic problems of thermodynamics. Brilliant flashes of understanding were followed by years of doubting, testing, and interpreting. Among the fundamental difficulties was a confusion between two concepts. One of these was the concept of energy. The other, which is related to the general concept of equilibrium and the direction of changes with respect to equilibrium, was stated first, but the language was such that it was long misunderstood and therefore rejected. It is now accepted as the second law of thermodynamics.

Very few people today who have any acquaintance with modern science would doubt the following generalizations:

1. Perpetual-motion machines don't work.
2. Bodies in equilibrium have the same temperature. When two bodies in contact have different temperatures, energy flows, as heat, from the warmer to the cooler body.
3. Bodies in equilibrium have the same pressure. When two bodies in contact, at the same temperature, have different pressures, the body at the higher pressure tends to expand and compress the body at the lower pressure.

THE SECOND LAW OF THERMODYNAMICS

None of these statements is required by the first law,[1] which requires energy balance in any process but does not say whether a process will actually occur. For example, both exothermic and endothermic reactions are known that do proceed without external forcing. There is, despite the variety in these generalizations, a similarity of pattern and intent—saying, for example, whether a specific process will or will not occur—that suggests a common basis. The basis will be found in the postulate known as *the second law of thermodynamics.*

The work done in any reversible process is the maximum work that can be done, at the given temperature, since the force opposing any motion can be, at most, nearly equal to the driving force.[2]

$$(T) \qquad\qquad w_{\mathrm{rev}} \geqslant w \qquad\qquad (1)$$

The heat absorbed is also a maximum for the reversible path.

$$(T) \qquad\qquad q_{\mathrm{rev}} = \Delta E + w_{\mathrm{rev}} \geqslant \Delta E + w = q \qquad\qquad (2)$$

For given initial and final states, ΔE is fixed and so are w_{rev} and q_{rev}. But if (at constant temperature) w_{rev} and q_{rev} are dependent only on the end points, they can be written as changes in state functions. Let $\Delta A = -w_{\mathrm{rev}}$ and $\Delta B = q_{\mathrm{rev}}$ for processes at constant temperature. Then

$$(T) \qquad\qquad \Delta E = \Delta A + \Delta B$$

and we can define A and B to satisfy the equation

$$E = A + B \qquad\qquad (3)$$

In any isothermal process in which the energy of the system changes by ΔE, only part of this energy change, equal to ΔA, can appear as work done by the system. Part of the energy change is prohibited from appearing as work. This second energy term, called ΔB for the moment, cannot be lost, because of the first law (conservation of energy); it is analogous to "spilled energy," which is lost for useful purposes during the transfer operation.

Entropy

From equation 3 two important functions are obtained. One, given the symbol A, is called the *Helmholtz free energy,* or sometimes the *work function,* and is characterized, as given above, by the constant-temperature equation

$$(T) \qquad\qquad \Delta A = -w_{\mathrm{rev}} \qquad\qquad (4)$$

This function, and an even more useful quantity derived from it, will be investigated later.

---

[1] The first law prohibits certain perpetual-motion machines, called "perpetual-motion machines of the first kind." The more interesting attempts, called "perpetual-motion machines of the second kind," do satisfy the first law.

[2] See footnotes, pp. 13 and 38.

The second function is obtained by dividing the temperature into the function B. That is, let $B = TS$, where S is a state function. Then

$$d(TS) = T\,dS + S\,dT$$

and at constant temperature

$$(T) \qquad\qquad d(TS) = T\,dS = \delta q_{rev}$$

or, quite generally,

$$dS = \frac{\delta q_{rev}}{T} \tag{5}$$

where δq_{rev} is the (infinitesimal) amount of heat absorbed by the system at the temperature T as the system follows a reversible path. The new function S is the one of interest. It is called the *entropy*. The important properties of entropy can be developed from equation 5, which shows how the entropy changes. In particular, the relationship of entropy to equilibrium and to spontaneous processes will be found in this way. Later, a look at the meaning of entropy at the molecular level will provide a more complete picture of this important quantity.

ENTROPY, EQUILIBRIUM, AND SPONTANEOUS CHANGE.   Consider the process of melting 1 gm of ice, at 0°C and 1 atm pressure, by bringing it into contact with a thermostat, or heat reservoir. This might be a very large block of metal, well insulated from its surroundings and large enough so that the reasonable amount of heat withdrawn will not change its temperature. For the ice,

$$\Delta S = \frac{q_{rev}}{T} = \frac{79.74 \text{ cal/gm}}{273.15°\text{K}} = 0.292 \text{ cal/gm-deg}$$

If the thermostat is at exactly the same temperature,

$$\Delta S_{thermostat} = \frac{-79.74 \text{ cal/gm (ice)}}{273.15°\text{K}} = -0.292 \text{ cal/gm-deg}$$

Taking the ice as the system and the thermostat as the surroundings, $(\Delta S)_{system+surroundings} = 0$. Thus far it might appear as if entropy also is conserved (compare equation 1, Chapter 1). But we know that unless there is at least a small temperature differential between the thermostat and the ice, the ice will not melt. We cannot melt an ice cube by bringing it into contact with a large block of ice; it must be touched to something warmer. If the temperature of the thermostat is higher than 273.15°K, $\Delta S_{thermostat}$ will be smaller in magnitude than ΔS_{ice}, and ΔS for the ice plus the thermostat, or system plus surroundings, will be positive. This is the essence of the second law of thermodynamics, which states

$$(\Delta S)_{system+surroundings} > 0 \tag{6}$$

for any process whatever that actually occurs. The similarity, and contrast, to the statement of the first law (equation 1, Chapter 1) should be noted. In the limit of a process that is truly reversible (for example, thermostat and ice at the same temperature, so that the ice can melt or refreeze by exchange of heat with the thermostat), the total entropy change will approach the value zero. Recognizing the importance of this limiting condition we may write

$$(\Delta S)_{\text{system+surroundings}} \geqslant 0 \qquad (6a)$$

with the understanding that the equality can be approached as closely as we wish, if we have sufficient patience.

From equation 6 or 6a, taken as a second basic postulate, it is possible to derive results that are well established from our experience. There are, in general, many different paths that a system may follow between any two specified states, of which at least one (actually, an infinite number) will be thermodynamically reversible. If $\delta q_1, \delta q_2, \ldots \delta q_{\text{rev}}$ are the various amounts of heat absorbed and $\delta w_1, \delta w_2, \ldots \delta w_{\text{rev}}$ the various amounts of work done along these paths, then, in general, $\delta q_1 \neq \delta q_2 \neq \cdots \neq \delta q_{\text{rev}}$ and $\delta w_1 \neq \delta w_2 \neq \cdots \neq \delta w_{\text{rev}}$. But dE is the same for each of these paths. That is, regardless of which path the system actually follows,

$$dE = \delta q_1 - \delta w_1 = \delta q_2 - \delta w_2 = \cdots = \delta q_{\text{rev}} - \delta w_{\text{rev}}$$

and, since $\delta q_{\text{rev}} = T\,dS$ and $\delta w_{\text{rev}} = P\,dV$ (if the only work is work of expansion or compression), it follows that, for any path,

$$dE = T\,dS - P\,dV \qquad (7)$$

This equation is valid for any process occurring in a system of constant composition. (If there is a change of chemical composition, as would be required if electrical work were produced, or a change of concentrations, additional terms should be added to equation 7.) At constant volume the second term of equation 7 becomes zero and we obtain

$$\left.\frac{\partial E}{\partial S}\right)_V = T \qquad (8)$$

or

$$\left.\frac{\partial S}{\partial E}\right)_V = \frac{1}{T} \qquad (8a)$$

FIGURE 1   *An isolated system is divided arbitrarily into two parts, of energies E_1 and E_2 and entropies S_1 and S_2.*

Take an arbitrary system that is isolated from its surroundings. The second law then requires that $dS \geqslant 0$ for any changes within this system. Divide the system into two parts in any fashion (Figure 1). For example, the total system might be a cup of water, which is considered to be divided into two equal parts, or it might be a bar of lead, with one cm³ in the center considered as one part and the re-

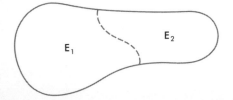

mainder as the second part. Let E_1 be the energy of the first part and E_2 the energy of the second part, and consider a flow of energy (as heat) from one part to the other, holding the two volumes constant. Because the total system is isolated.

$$dE = dE_1 + dE_2 = 0 \tag{9}$$
$$dE_1 = -dE_2$$

The total entropy change, dS, arising from a flow of energy between the two parts, is

$$dS = \frac{dS}{dE_1} dE_1 = \frac{dS_1}{dE_1} dE_1 + \frac{dS_2}{dE_1} dE_1$$
$$= \frac{dS_1}{dE_1} dE_1 - \frac{dS_2}{dE_2} dE_1 \tag{10}$$

Substitution of equation 8a and application of the second law gives

$$dS = \left(\frac{1}{T_1} - \frac{1}{T_2}\right) dE_1 \geqslant 0 \tag{11}$$

The necessary condition for equilibrium is that $dS = 0$ for the process in which $\delta q_1 = dE_1$ flows between the two parts. This can be satisfied only if $T_1 = T_2$. This proves that bodies in equilibrium have the same temperature.

Suppose that $T_1 > T_2$. Then $(1/T_1 - 1/T_2)$ is negative and dE_1 must also be negative, showing that part one loses energy to part two. This proves that when two bodies in contact have different temperatures, energy flows, as heat, from the warmer to the cooler body.

From equation 7 we can derive a relationship for the dependence of entropy on volume.

$$dS = \frac{1}{T} dE + \frac{P}{T} dV$$

and therefore

$$\left.\frac{\partial S}{\partial V}\right)_E = \frac{P}{T} \tag{12}$$

Again consider the isolated total system of Figure 1 and assume it to have a uniform temperature. Then, as before, we can write the total change in entropy that might result from a change in volume in the form

$$dS = \frac{dS_1}{dV_1} dV_1 + \frac{dS_2}{dV_1} dV_1$$

and, since $dV_1 = -dV_2$, substitution of equation 12 gives[3]

$$dS = \left(\frac{P_1}{T_1} - \frac{P_2}{T_2}\right) dV_1 \geqslant 0 \tag{13}$$

---

[3] It is assumed that $T_1 = T_2$ and thus the total entropy is unchanged by an exchange of energy as heat between the two parts. Any work done by one part on the other can be compensated by such a heat flow, so the constant-energy restriction of equation 12 is satisfied.

This proves that two bodies in equilibrium must have not only the same temperature but also the same pressure. It also proves that, when two bodies in contact, at the same temperature, have different pressures, the body at the higher pressure will tend to expand and compress the body at the lower pressure.

ISOTHERMAL ENTROPY CHANGES. Entropy changes at a single temperature follow quite directly from equation 5. Calculations involving a temperature difference or temperature change will be treated later.

A change of phase, under equilibrium conditions, will be at constant temperature and constant pressure. The heat absorbed will be equal to ΔH. Therefore,

$$\Delta S = \frac{\Delta H}{T} \tag{14}$$

For example, the entropy change for the melting of ice was found to be 0.292 cal/gm-deg or 5.26 cal/mole-deg. The entropy of vaporization of water at 100°C is

$$\Delta S_{\text{vap}} = \frac{539.7 \times 18}{373.15} = 26.0 \text{ cal/mole-deg}$$

More typical liquids, not involving such strong intermolecular forces, have ΔS_{vap} values of about 22 cal/mole-deg at their normal boiling points. This is known as *Trouton's rule*.

The work done in a reversible, isothermal expansion of an ideal gas was found to be (equation 10, Chapter 1) $w_{\text{rev}} = nRT \ln V_2/V_1$. For an ideal gas at constant temperature $\Delta E = 0$ and therefore $q_{\text{rev}} = w_{\text{rev}}$. The entropy change is thus

$$(T, \text{I.G., rev.}) \qquad \Delta S = \frac{q_{\text{rev}}}{T} = nR \ln V_2/V_1 \tag{15}$$

If the gas expands, through a pinhole or stopcock, into an evacuated container (Figure 2), no work is done, and if the containers are insulated, no heat will be absorbed. The energy is unchanged and therefore, if the gas is ideal, the temperature will remain constant. This serves as an experimental demonstration (performed by Joule, in 1844) of the dependence of energy only on the temperature, although it is not as sensitive as a later

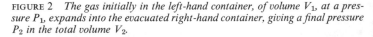

FIGURE 2 *The gas initially in the left-hand container, of volume V_1, at a pressure P_1, expands into the evacuated right-hand container, giving a final pressure P_2 in the total volume V_2.*

method by Joule and Thomson. The entropy change of an ideal gas in such an irreversible, adiabatic[4] expansion can be calculated as follows.

Entropy is a state function, so the entropy change depends only on the initial state and the final state. Entropy changes are independent of the path taken between the initial and final states. When an ideal gas expands at constant temperature from V_1 to V_2, the final state is the same whether the process is reversible or irreversible. Therefore, the entropy change for the adiabatic expansion of the ideal gas into a vacuum is

(I.G., T) $$\Delta S = nR \ln V_2/V_1 \qquad (16)$$

even though $q = w = 0$ in this process.

The example just cited illustrates a general method for evaluating entropy changes in irreversible processes. Having determined what are the initial and final states, a path is found between those states that will be entirely reversible. Then, using equation 5, $\Delta S = q_{rev}/T$.

It is of interest to calculate the entropy change for the surroundings in the reversible and irreversible expansions above. In the reversible expansion, $q = q_{rev} = -q_{surr} = -(q_{rev})_{surr}$. Therefore,

$$\Delta S_{surr} = -nR \ln V_2/V_1$$

The adiabatic expansion into a vacuum produces no change at all in the surroundings, and therefore

$$\Delta S_{surr} = 0$$

Adding together the entropy changes for system and surroundings, we obtain, for the reversible expansion,

$$(\Delta S)_{system+surroundings} = 0$$

and for the irreversible expansion, into a vacuum,

$$(\Delta S)_{system+surroundings} = nR \ln V_2/V_1 > 0$$

This result agrees with the requirements of the second law.

The particular irreversible path chosen is an extreme case. If the gas had been allowed to expand against a constant external pressure (as in Figure 1, Chapter 1) the entropy change for system plus surroundings would have been positive, but less than that for the expansion into a vacuum. The magnitude of the total entropy change (system plus surroundings) can be taken as a measure of the degree of thermodynamic irreversibility of any process.

INTERPRETATION OF ENTROPY.   The thermodynamic equations tell us how to calculate entropy changes and tell us that entropy is a property, or state function, of matter that always tends to increase, considering the

---

[4] The term *adiabatic,* as applied in chemical thermodynamics, implies that there is no heat exchange between the system and its surroundings. This can be achieved, in practice, (1) by insulating the system, (2) by maintaining the immediate surroundings at the same temperature as the system, or (3) by carrying out the process very rapidly.

known universe as a whole. Thermodynamics gives no picture of what entropy means at the molecular level. Statistical mechanics, on the other hand, is built upon a molecular interpretation of entropy. Without attempting to present, at this point, the mathematical arguments of statistical mechanics, it may be observed that entropy is a direct, quantitative measure of the relative probability of a particular state of a system and is, at the same time, a measure of the disorder, or randomness, of the state. A few examples will illustrate the concept.

In Figure 2, the molecules of the gas are collected together in one container. When the stopcock has been opened, this initial state becomes a very improbable state; the most probable state is when the gas molecules have been randomly, or evenly, distributed between the two containers. The entropy of the latter state is larger by $nR \ln V_2/V_1$ than the entropy of the former state. A crystal of salt plus a cup of water will have a lower combined entropy than the solution formed when the salt disperses, or dissolves, in the water. Magnetized iron has a more ordered arrangement of its parts than has nonmagnetized iron; the magnetic iron has a lower entropy.

As temperature increases, bodies absorb heat and increase in entropy. Thus at high temperatures we expect to find high-entropy states. Water molecules fly about all available space rather than sitting neatly arranged in ice crystals; iron becomes demagnetized; solids dissolve in liquids. When the temperature (of the system) is decreased, the entropy (of the system) must be decreased and ordered arrangements are formed once more.

An ordered arrangement also implies that the positions of particles are known in more detail than for a random arrangement. This analogy between information and entropy has been shown to be of fundamental significance. It has given rise to the new field of "information theory," which has provided further insight into the meanings of both entropy and information, and into the principles involved in the accumulation, transfer, storage, and retrieval of information.

Gibbs Free Energy

The Helmholtz free energy, A, is called "free energy" because it is the change in A that represents the maximum amount of energy available to perform work in any isothermal process (equation 4). Like entropy, it can be employed as a measure of whether the system is at equilibrium or, if not, which way any process must go to approach equilibrium. However, as for the energy, E, corrections are often required for work done against a constant pressure. Just as enthalpy, H, is found to be more convenient than E for most laboratory applications of the first law, a new function, G, called the Gibbs free energy,[5] is usually more convenient than A for applications of the second law.

---

[5] For many years the Gibbs free energy and the Helmholtz free energy were not clearly distinguished. As a consequence, both acquired the symbol F, the former especially in the United States and the latter mainly in other parts of the world. The symbols G and A are becoming widely adopted to avoid this confusion, although some authors continue to retain F for one or the other. In this book, the term "free energy" will always mean the Gibbs free energy, unless otherwise noted.

The relationships between the fundamental thermodynamic functions can be given in the form of equations (equations 17-19) or, more descriptively, in a figure (Figure 3).

$$H = E + PV \tag{17}$$

$$A = E - TS \tag{18}$$

$$G = H - TS \tag{19}$$

$$G = A + PV \tag{19a}$$

$$G = E + PV - TS \tag{19b}$$

FREE ENERGY AND EQUILIBRIUM. The entropy suffers from an important inconvenience for determinations of equilibrium. Unless the system is totally isolated, one must calculate the entropy of both the system and the surroundings to apply the second law, even though we are interested only in the system. The Gibbs free energy corrects for interactions with the surroundings, if the temperature and pressure are constant. (If T and V are fixed, A is more appropriate.) A series of important equations, dealing with variations of free energy and with criteria for equilibrium, will be obtained. Assume for the present that the only work done is work of expansion or compression and that the composition of the system does not change.

From equation 19b,

$$dG = dE + d(PV) - d(TS)$$

As noted earlier, $dE = \delta q - \delta w = \delta q_{rev} - \delta w_{rev}$, regardless of path. We may therefore substitute $\delta q_{rev} - \delta w_{rev}$ for dE, to obtain

$$dG = \delta q_{rev} - \delta w_{rev} + P\,dV + V\,dP - T\,dS - S\,dT \tag{20}$$

But $\delta q_{rev} = T\,dS$ and $\delta w_{rev} = P\,dV$. Therefore, quite generally,

$$dG = V\,dP - S\,dT \tag{21}$$

Two extremely useful equations are obtained by holding constant first the temperature and then the pressure:

$$\left.\frac{\partial G}{\partial P}\right)_T = V \tag{22}$$

$$\left.\frac{\partial G}{\partial T}\right)_P = -S \tag{23}$$

It should be noted as a memory aid that P and V go together, as do T and S.

An equally valid variation of equation 20 is obtained by the substitution $dE = \delta q - \delta w$, giving

$$dG = \delta q - \delta w + P\,dV + V\,dP - T\,dS - S\,dT$$

FIGURE 3 *The relationships between E, H, A, and G involve P, V, T, and S, as given by equations 17-19.*

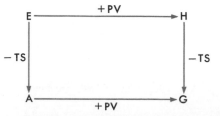

—which reduces, for constant temperature and pressure, to

$$(T, P) \qquad dG = \delta q - \delta w + P \, dV - T \, dS \qquad (24)$$

But at constant pressure, the pressure of the system must equal the pressure of the surroundings, so $\delta w = P \, dV$, and at constant temperature $q_{rev} \geqslant q$ (equation 2).[6] Therefore,

$$(T, P) \qquad dG = \delta q - T \, dS = \delta q - \delta q_{rev} \leqslant 0$$

Thus

$$(T, P) \qquad dG \leqslant 0 \qquad (25)$$

in general, and for the limiting case of the reversible, or equilibrium process

$$(T, P, \text{rev}) \qquad dG = 0 \qquad (25a)$$

This shows that ΔG must be negative, or, in the limit of a reversible process, zero. That is, G is a minimum for an equilibrium state. This is the more convenient criterion for equilibrium that was sought.

Returning now to equation 20, assume temperature and pressure are constant. Then

$$dG = P \, dV - \delta w_{rev}$$

If the only work is work of expansion we obtain equation 25a, but more generally

$$(T, P) \qquad dG = -\delta w'_{rev} \qquad (26)$$

where $\delta w'_{rev} = \delta w_{rev} - P \, dV$ is work that is done other than work against the constant pressure. For example, in an electrochemical cell, w' would be the electrical work done, or the "electrical energy produced," by the reaction. Work against a gravitational field or against a magnetic field would also be included in w'.

IDEAL-GAS EXPANSIONS. The change in free energy of an ideal gas in an isothermal expansion or compression is particularly important because it

---

[6] A general proof of equation 2 is obtained directly from the assumption of the second law. Very briefly,

$$(dS)_{\text{syst+surr}} = \frac{\delta q_{rev}}{T} + \frac{(\delta q_{rev})_{\text{surr}}}{T_{\text{surr}}} \geqslant 0$$

This inequality is still valid, for any process occurring in the system, if $(\delta q)_{\text{surr}} = (\delta q_{rev})_{\text{surr}}$, which may therefore be assumed without loss of generality. But $(\delta q)_{\text{surr}} = -\delta q$, and $T_{\text{surr}} = T$ because temperature is constant. Therefore,

$$(dS)_{\text{syst+surr}} = \frac{\delta q_{rev}}{T} - \frac{\delta q}{T} \geqslant 0 \text{ and } \delta q_{rev} \geqslant \delta q$$

It follows from this that $w_{rev} \geqslant w$ at constant temperature.

has been found possible to express free energy changes of all systems, whether gases or not, in this same form. The broader theory will be developed in the discussion of physical equilibria.

We start with the definition of G, equation 19. At constant temperature,

$$(T) \qquad\qquad \Delta G = \Delta H - T \Delta S \qquad\qquad (27)$$

In an isothermal, reversible expansion of an ideal gas, $\Delta E = 0$ and $\Delta H = 0$.

$$q_{rev} = w_{rev} = \int nRT\, dV/V = nRT \ln V_2/V_1$$
$$\Delta S = q_{rev}/T = nR \ln V_2/V_1$$
$$\Delta G = -T \Delta S = -nRT \ln V_2/V_1$$

or

$$(T, \text{I.G.}) \qquad\qquad \Delta G = nRT \ln P_2/P_1 \qquad\qquad (28)$$

The same result could be obtained from equation 22.

$$\Delta G = \int dG = \int \left(\frac{\partial G}{\partial P}\right)_T dP = \int V\, dP = \int nRT\, dP/P = nRT \ln P_2/P_1$$

FREE-ENERGY CHANGES IN CHEMICAL REACTIONS.   One of the very important applications of the free-energy function is to chemical reactions. Free energies can be added and subtracted in the same manner as enthalpies, since G is also a state function. Although no absolute values can be known for G, it is nevertheless possible to assign values relative to the elements, as was done for enthalpy values.[7] For example, the free-energy change for the oxidation of sulfur dioxide can be found as follows.

$$SO_2 + \tfrac{1}{2} O_2 \longrightarrow SO_3$$

$$\Delta G = G(SO_3) - G(SO_2) - G(\tfrac{1}{2} O_2)$$

$$= [G(SO_3) - G(S) - G(\tfrac{3}{2} O_2)] - [G(SO_2) - G(S) - G(O_2)]$$
$$\qquad\qquad\qquad\qquad\qquad\qquad - [G(\tfrac{1}{2} O_2) - G(\tfrac{1}{2} O_2)]$$

$$= \Delta G_{form}(SO_3) - \Delta G_{form}(SO_2) - \Delta G_{form}(\tfrac{1}{2} O_2)$$

Values for the free energy of formation can be found in handbook tables. In the example above, the free energies of formation when the reactants (the elements) and the products are in their standard states are $\Delta G_f^\circ(SO_3) = -88,520$ cal/mole and $\Delta G_f^\circ(SO_2) = -71,740$ cal/mole. Free energies of formation of elements are, by definition, zero. The free-energy change for the oxidation of SO_2 to SO_3 is thus $-88,520 - (-71,740) = -16,780$ cal/mole. The negative value indicates that SO_2 will combine with oxygen to form SO_3, at least in the presence of a suitable catalyst.

Free energies of formation of a few compounds are given in Table 1.

---

[7] An important difference in the assignment of standard states for G as compared to H will be discussed later. It is of no immediate concern.

THE SECOND LAW OF THERMODYNAMICS

These are evaluated for all substances in their standard states and are called *standard free energies of formation,* or simply *standard free energies.*

It should be mentioned again that thermodynamics is not concerned with rates. The conversion of diamond to graphite is thermodynamically allowed at room temperature and pressure, but of course does not happen. Even the reaction of hydrogen and oxygen does not occur upon mixing of the dry gases without a catalyst or external initiation. Any process that is permitted ($\Delta G < 0$) is called "spontaneous"; this term must **not** be confused with the word "instantaneous."

LECHATELIER'S PRINCIPLE AND EQUILIBRIUM. For every chemical reaction there exists an equilibrium point at which there is no further tendency for the reaction to proceed forward or backward. Although the equilibrium point of most reactions is far to one side or the other, a true equilibrium point can be calculated, and for nearly all systems the equilibrium point

Table 1   STANDARD ENTHALPIES AND FREE ENERGIES OF FORMATION*

Compound	State	$\Delta H_f°$	$\Delta G_f°$	Compound	State	$\Delta H_f°$	$\Delta G_f°$
AgBr	c	−23,780	−22,930	HI	g	6,300	376
AgCl	c	−30,362	−26,224		aq	−13,370	−12,350
AgI	c	−14,910	−15,850	H_2O	g	−57,798	−54,636
Ag_2O	c	−7,306	−2,586		lq	−68,317	−56,690
Al_2O_3	c	−400,400	−378,000	H_2O_2	g	−32,530	−25,200
Br_2	g	7,390	750		lq	−44,840	−28,200
	diamond	453	685	H_2S	g	−4,815	−7,890
				I_2	g	14,900	4,630
C	g	−220,500	−209,827	NH_3	g	−11,040	−3,966
CF_4	g	−25,940	−15,833		aq	−19,320	−6,370
CCl_4	lq	−33,300	−16,400	NH_4Cl	c	−75,380	−48,730
CO	g	−26,417	−32,783	N_2O	g	19,610	24,900
CO_2	g	−94,052	−94,265	NO	g	21,580	20,700
	aq	−98,690	−92,310	NO_2	g	7,900	12,250
$CaCO_3$	calcite	−288,450	−269,780	N_2O_4	g	2,170	23,360
	aragonite	−288,490	−269,530	NaCl	c	−98,260	−91,790
$CaCl_2$	c	−190,000	−179,300		aq	−97,302	−93,939
	aq	−209,820	−194,880	NaOH	c	−102,240	−91,190
CaF_2	c	−290,300	−277,700		aq	−112,236	−100,184
	aq	−287,090	−264,340	O_3	g	34,100	39,000
CaO	c	−151,900	−144,400	SO_2	g	−70,960	−71,740
$Ca(OH)_2$	c	−235,800	−214,330	SO_3	g	−94,450	−88,520
	aq	−239,680	−207,370	C_2H_2	g	54,200	50,000
FeO	c	−63,700	−58,400	C_2H_4	g	12,500	16,280
Fe_2O_3	c	−196,500	−177,100	C_2H_6	g	−20,236	−7,860
Fe_3O_4	c	−267,000	−242,400	CH_3OH	g	−48,080	−38,690
HBr	g	−8,660	−12,730		lq	−57,020	−39,730
HCl	g	−22,060	−22,780	C_2H_5OH	g	−56,240	−40,300
	aq	−40,023	−31,350		lq	−66,356	−41,770
HF	g	−64,800	−65,300	C_6H_6	lq	19,820	30,989

* Values are in cal/mole, for 25°C, 1 atm, and are taken from Circular 500, National Bureau of Standards, "Selected Values of Chemical Thermodynamic Properties," or from the JANAF Tables. Not all zeros shown are significant but values are given in calories to emphasize the order of magnitude of these quantities in relation to other values discussed.

The standard states for liquids (lq) and crystalline solids (c) are the pure materials at 1 atm pressure and the standard states for gases (g) are the pure gases at 1 atm pressure in the "ideal gas state" (that is, extrapolated from low pressures assuming ideal gas behavior). "aq" refers to the (hypothetical ideal) 1 molal solution in water.

can be demonstrated if the experimental techniques are sufficiently sensitive.

LeChatelier's principle states that when any stress is applied to a system at equilibrium, the system will respond in a manner that will reduce the stress. For example, the reaction

$$2 \text{ NO} + \text{O}_2 \longrightarrow 2 \text{ NO}_2$$

produces heat ($\Delta H = -13,510$ cal/mole (NO_2)) but causes a decrease of volume, or pressure. Therefore an increase of temperature will tend to drive the reaction to the left, so that the reaction will absorb heat, but an increase of pressure, by compression, will tend to drive the reaction to the right to decrease the number of moles of gas and hence the pressure. These relationships can be derived, quantitatively, from the second law.

The change in $\Delta G_{\text{reaction}} = G_{\text{products}} - G_{\text{reactants}}$ with change of pressure is

$$\frac{\partial \Delta G}{\partial P}\bigg)_T = \frac{\partial (G_{\text{products}} - G_{\text{reactants}})}{\partial P}\bigg)_T$$

The derivative of the sum is the sum of the derivatives:

$$\frac{\partial \Delta G}{\partial P}\bigg)_T = \frac{\partial G_{\text{products}}}{\partial P}\bigg)_T - \frac{\partial G_{\text{reactants}}}{\partial P}\bigg)_T$$

From equation 22, these derivatives are the respective volumes:

$$\frac{\partial \Delta G}{\partial P}\bigg)_T = V_{\text{products}} - V_{\text{reactants}}$$

or

$$\frac{\partial \Delta G}{\partial P}\bigg)_T = \Delta V \tag{29}$$

Similarly, from equation 23,

$$\frac{\partial \Delta G}{\partial T}\bigg)_P = -\Delta S \tag{30}$$

This equation tells how ΔG (measured at some constant temperature and pressure) depends upon the temperature at which the process occurs. The ΔS on the right-hand side is similarly to be measured at a constant pressure and at a constant temperature (the temperature at which the derivative, or the slope of ΔG vs. T, is determined). We may therefore substitute for ΔS the quantity $(\Delta G - \Delta H)/T$.

$$\frac{\partial \Delta G}{\partial T}\bigg)_P = \frac{\Delta G - \Delta H}{T} \tag{30a}$$

To find the shift of equilibrium point we set $\Delta G = 0$ and obtain

$$\frac{\partial \Delta G}{\partial T}\bigg)_P = -\frac{\Delta H}{T} \tag{31}$$

The first result, equation 29, says that if there is a volume increase during the process, a pressure increase will cause an increase in ΔG, making the process less spontaneous. The second equation (31) says that if the process is endothermic (ΔH positive), a temperature increase will make ΔG more negative, thus making the process more spontaneous. The equations apply to phase changes or other equilibrium processes as well as to chemical reactions.[8] The importance of the equations is that they give a quantitative description of how ΔG changes, and therefore of how the equilibrium point changes.

Free Energy and the Energy-Entropy Battle

For the decomposition of ammonia, we may write the equation

$$NH_3 \longrightarrow \tfrac{1}{2} N_2 + \tfrac{3}{2} H_2$$

$\Delta G = 3,976$ cal/mole, $\Delta H = 11,040$ cal/mole, and $\Delta S = 23.70$ cal/mole-deg. Assuming for the moment that ΔH and ΔS are independent of temperature, one could write

$$\Delta G = 11,040 - T \times 23.70$$

and at $298°$ K, $\Delta G = 11,040 - 298 \times 23.70 = 3,976$ cal/mole. It is clear that an increase in temperature would make the second term larger than the first and thus make ΔG negative. This would then be another example of a spontaneous endothermic reaction. (Although ΔH and ΔS are not independent of temperature, they do change slowly with temperature and at high temperatures $T \Delta S$ does become as large as ΔH for dissociation reactions.)

We tend to think of processes going in the direction of lower energy. Hydrogen and oxygen give off energy as they combine, sodium and chlorine give off energy as they combine, etc. But this tendency can be upset when there is an appreciable increase in entropy, as in the solution of a solid in a liquid. At higher temperatures, entropy predominates; at low temperatures the energy (or enthalpy) rules.

Entropy differences can be calculated from statistical mechanics. Very qualitatively, a dissociation reaction leads to greater disorder, or randomness. Similarly, vaporization leads to greater entropy. The entropy increase corresponding to the formation of 1 mole of gas molecules is on the order of magnitude of 30 cal/mole-deg (compare Trouton's rule, p. 34). At room temperature this would give a difference between enthalpy and free energy on the order of 10,000 cal per mole of gas formed. This is a small term compared to the enthalpy change of very exothermic reactions, such as most combustions are, but it is not small for many other reactions.

Entropies of reaction for a few representative chemical reactions are given in Table 2.

---

[8] It is assumed that there are no other changes that might cause a reverse effect. For example, changes in the relative concentrations of the reactants, or addition of an inert gas, are not within the scope of equations 29 and 30.

Table 2 STANDARD ENTROPIES OF REACTION, 25°C

Reaction		$\Delta S°$, cal/mole-deg
$2\,Al(c) + \frac{3}{2}\,O_2$	$\longrightarrow Al_2O_3(c)$	− 74.87
$C(gr) + O_2$	$\longrightarrow CO_2$	+ 0.71
$CO + \frac{1}{2}\,O_2$	$\longrightarrow CO_2$	− 20.64
$H_2 + Cl_2$	$\longrightarrow 2\,HCl$	+ 4.69
$H_2 + F_2$	$\longrightarrow 2\,HF$	+ 3.36
$H_2 + I_2(c)$	$\longrightarrow 2\,HI$	+39.73
$H_2 + \frac{1}{2}\,O_2$	$\longrightarrow H_2O\,(liq)$	− 38.99
$H_2 + S(rh)$	$\longrightarrow H_2S$	+10.31
$H_2 + 3\,N_2$	$\longrightarrow 2\,NH_3$	− 76.59
$S(rh) + O_2$	$\longrightarrow SO_2$	+ 2.67
$3\,C_2H_2$	$\longrightarrow C_6H_6\,(liq)$	− 79.67

Entropy Changes with Change of Temperature

The fundamental equation for entropy change, equation 5, gives the infinitesimal entropy increase for the absorption of an infinitesimal amount of heat at some temperature T. If the temperature changes continuously during the process, the sum of the entropy changes can be written as the integral

$$\Delta S = \int dS = \int \frac{\delta q_{rev}}{T} \tag{32}$$

It is not at all obvious from equation 32 how this integral is to be evaluated, but it can be handled quite easily as follows:

$$\Delta S = \int \frac{\delta q_{rev}}{T} = \int \frac{\delta q_{rev}}{T} \frac{dT}{dT} = \int \frac{\delta q_{rev}}{dT} \frac{dT}{T} = \int C \frac{dT}{T} \tag{33}$$

The heat capacity, C, is often nearly independent of temperature (over temperature intervals of tens of degrees) so the equation can be simplified to the form

$$\Delta S = C \ln \frac{T_2}{T_1} \tag{34}$$

Note that the heat capacity has not been given a subscript in equations 33 or 34; this is because no conditions such as constant pressure or constant volume have thus far been specified. If pressure is constant, C_P is inserted in these equations; if volume is constant, C_V is required. If neither pressure nor volume is constant, it may be necessary to find an alternate path consisting of constant pressure and constant temperature segments, or constant volume and constant temperature segments. It may be, too, that it will be simpler to return to equation 32. For example, in a reversible, adiabatic expansion or compression, $\delta q = \delta q_{rev} = 0$, and therefore it is clear that the integral, and the entropy change, must be identically zero; in order to apply equation 34 one would have to define an "adiabatic heat capacity" that would always be zero.

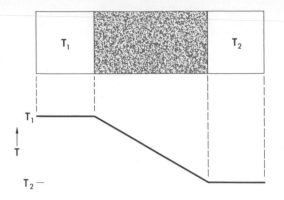

FIGURE 4 *The left-hand body is at a temperature T_1, the right-hand body at T_2, and the thermal insulator between will vary in temperature, along its length, between these values when a steady state has been achieved.*

The entropy change for the transfer of energy, as heat, between two bodies at different temperatures requires a different approach. In Figure 4, the body at the left is at a temperature T_1, the body at the right is at a lower temperature T_2, and each body is assumed large enough that its temperature will not be appreciably affected by the heat flow considered.

One method of solving this problem is to add a thermal insulator connecting the two bodies. When a steady state has been achieved, the temperature will vary continuously with the distance, as shown in the lower part of Figure 4, but the temperature will be constant at any point in the system even though a small amount of heat is flowing past each point. The entropy change is the sum of three terms: the entropy change of the left-hand body at T_1; the entropy change for the insulator; and the entropy change for the right-hand body at temperature T_2.

$$\Delta S = \Delta S_1 + \Delta S_{\text{insulator}} + \Delta S_2$$

For a heat flow of magnitude q, the first term is

$$\Delta S_1 = \frac{-q}{T_1}$$

where ΔS_1 is the entropy change of the body at T_1. Similarly, the entropy change for the body at temperature T_2 is

$$\Delta S_2 = \frac{q}{T_2}$$

The insulator may be considered part of the surroundings and need not be further included in the calculation for the system.[9] Then for the system, which consists of the two bodies at the two temperatures,

$$\Delta S = \Delta S_1 + \Delta S_2 = \frac{-q}{T_1} + \frac{q}{T_2} = q\left(\frac{1}{T_2} - \frac{1}{T_1}\right) > 0 \qquad (35)$$

It is clear that the thermal insulator added to the problem of Figure 4

---

[9] Actually, the entropy change of the insulator is zero, because the state of the insulator is not changing.

plays no real part in the calculation. It can make no difference whatever to the state, or the entropy, of a body that loses a given amount of heat at the temperature T_1 what happens to this energy after it is gone. Similarly, to the body absorbing a certain amount of heat at the temperature T_2, it can make no difference to the state, or entropy, of the body, where the energy came from.

Equation 35 can be applied to the problem of radiation emitted by one body and absorbed, without performance of work, by another body. This treatment also provides a clearer justification for the paragraph preceding equation 6, in which heat is transferred to the system (ice) from the surroundings (thermostat) at a slightly higher temperature.

Problems

1. Figure 5 shows a capillary tube dipping into a dish of water. The tubing is bent, and water dripping from the suspended open end turns a paddle wheel before returning to the dish. By covering the apparatus, water can be retained and the energy required is returned to the dish by thermal conduction from the surroundings. What is wrong?

2. Figure 6 shows a wheel on which are mounted small bar magnets. The force between the fixed magnet and the individual magnets attached to the wheel may be taken as proportional to $1/d$, where d is the distance separating the magnets. Show that the force between the fixed magnet and the nearest magnet is smaller than the sum of the forces pulling the magnets along the right-hand side. That is, $1/d_1 < 1/d_2 + 1/d_3 + \cdots$. A magnetic shield (readily available) is placed as shown. The wheel then rotates counterclockwise. What is wrong?

3. Two moles of an ideal gas at 25°C is expanded into a vacuum to 10 times its original volume. Find ΔS.

4. A vessel containing 5 moles of an ideal gas, A, is connected to an identical vessel containing 5 moles of another ideal gas, B, and the two are allowed to reach equilibrium. For this process, at 27°C, find
   a. ΔS for the gas A
   b. ΔS for the gas B
   c. ΔS for the entire system $(\Delta S(A) + \Delta S(B))$.
   d. What would ΔS be if A and B were the same gas?

FIGURE 5 *A perpetual-motion machine employing capillary action.*

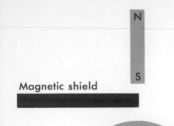

Magnetic shield

FIGURE 6 *Each small magnet on the wheel is aligned with its north pole outward in this perpetual-motion machine.*

5. If a gas at pressure P and volume V_1 is mixed isothermally with another gas at pressure P and volume V_2 to give a mixture at pressure P and volume $V = V_1 + V_2$, the mole fractions are $N_1 = V_1/(V_1 + V_2)$ and $N_2 = V_2/(V_1 + V_2)$. Show that the "entropy of mixing" of ideal gases in this fashion is

$$\Delta S = -nR \sum_i N_i \ln N_i$$

where $n = \Sigma n_i$ is the total number of moles and $N_i = n_i/n$ is the mole fraction of the ith gas.

6. A vessel containing 5 moles of an ideal gas, A, is connected to an identical vessel containing 10 moles of an ideal gas, B, and the two are allowed to reach equilibrium. For the process, at $27°C$, find
   a. ΔS, assuming A and B are different gases.
   b. ΔS, assuming A and B are the same. Explain the distinction between these two cases and between these and problem 4.

7. Which of the following have the higher value of S?
   a. CO_2 at $25°C$, 1 atm   or "dry ice" at 1 atm
   b. a coiled spring   or the spring "relaxed"
   c. 1 gm of liquid water at $25°C$ or 1 gm of water vapor, at the vapor pressure of water at $25°C$
   d. silica glass   or quartz (crystalline silica)

8. When a gas escapes through a pinhole into an evacuated chamber, the first gas to escape is later compressed by the following gas. Yet it is stated that $w = 0$. Explain.

9. Calculate ΔG for the processes described in problems 3, 4, and 6.

10. The heat of vaporization of cyclohexane, C_6H_{12}, is 86 cal/gm at its normal boiling point, $80.7°C$.
    a. Calculate ΔS for the vaporization of 1 mole of cyclohexane at $80.7°C$ and 1 atm. Compare with the Trouton constant.
    b. Calculate ΔG for the same process.

11. Calculate the free-energy change when 3 moles of Ar is compressed isothermally from 2 to 6 atm at $50°C$.

12. The standard free energies of formation of ethylene (C_2H_4) and of ethane (C_2H_6) at $25°C$ and 1 atm are 16,282 and $-7,860$ cal/mole. The standard enthalpies of formation are 12,496 and $-20,236$ cal/mole. For the reduction of ethylene with H_2 to give ethane,
    a. find $\Delta G°$
    b. find $\Delta S°$

13. Calculate $\Delta S°$, the entropy change under standard conditions at $25°C$, for the reaction of carbon (graphite) with fluorine gas to give the gas CF_4, using values as necessary from Table 1.

14. For each of the following reactions at $25°C$ calculate (using Table 1)

    a. $\Delta H°$ b. $\Delta G°$ c. $\Delta S°$

$$4\, FeO + O_2 \longrightarrow 2\, Fe_2O_3$$
$$2\, Fe_3O_4 + \tfrac{1}{2} O_2 \longrightarrow 3\, Fe_2O_3$$
$$3\, FeO + \tfrac{1}{2} O_2 \longrightarrow Fe_3O_4$$

Which form of iron oxide—FeO, Fe_3O_4, or Fe_2O_3—is most stable in the presence of an oxygen atmosphere at this temperature? Explain.

15. Would Fe_3O_4 (see problem 14) become more or less stable, with respect to FeO and oxygen, as temperature is increased? Explain.

16. The equilibrium point for the reaction

$$3 H_2 + N_2 \longrightarrow 2 NH_3$$

is well to the right at room temperature and at atmospheric pressures for the reactants.

    a. Is the production of ammonia affected favorably or unfavorably by an increase of T? By an increase of P?

    b. Can you suggest, on the basis of these answers, why the reaction is run commercially at high temperature and high pressure?

17. In the following reactions, would you expect ΔS to be positive or negative? Explain.

    a. $Ag_2O(s) \longrightarrow 2 Ag(s) + \frac{1}{2} O_2(g)$

    b. $2 CO(g) + O_2(g) \longrightarrow 2 CO_2(g)$

    c. $2 C(s) + O_2(g) \longrightarrow 2 CO(g)$

    d. $CaH_2(s) + 2 H_2O(l) \longrightarrow Ca(OH)_2(s) + H_2(g)$

    e. $H_2(g) + I_2(s) \longrightarrow 2 HI(g)$

    f. $2 H_2(g) + O_2(g) \longrightarrow 2 H_2O(l)$

    g. $n\, C_2H_4(g) \longrightarrow -(C_2H_4)_n -$ (polyethylene)

18. A Dewar flask contains 500 ml of water at 25°C. To the flask is added 100 gm of ice at -6°C. For the process which then occurs, find

    a. ΔH

    b. ΔS

    c. the final temperature

19. Find

    a. ΔS b. ΔH c. ΔE

for the process of subliming 5 gm of ice at -10°C and warming the vapor to 200°C and 4 atm.

20. One kilowatt hour of energy passes from a heater, at a temperature of 1000°K, to a room at 27°C. Find ΔS

    a. in joule/deg

    b. in cal/deg

21. For the freezing of 5 gm of supercooled water, at -10°C, to ice at -10°C, calculate

    a. ΔH b. ΔS c. ΔG

22. The standard free energies (1 atm) of NO_2 and N_2O_4 at 25°C are 12,270 and 23,440 cal/mole. For the reaction

$$2 NO_2(1\ atm) \longrightarrow N_2O_4(P\ atm)$$

    a. find ΔG if $P = 1$

    b. find the value of P (that is, the pressure of N_2O_4) that would make $\Delta G = 0$

23. In a reversible, adiabatic expansion, $\delta q = 0$. Show, by setting $dE = n\, C_V dT$ and $\delta w = P\, dV$ that, if $P = nRT/V$, the equation $\delta w = -dE$ can be integrated (after dividing through by T to separate variables) to give

    (I. G., rev, adiabatic) $C_V \ln \dfrac{T_2}{T_1} = R \ln \dfrac{V_1}{V_2}$ (36)

24. Show that, by replacing dV by $d(nRT/P)$, the equation for a reversible, adiabatic expansion integrates (after separating variables) to give

$$\text{(I. G., rev, adiabatic)} \quad C_P \ln \frac{T_2}{T_1} = R \ln \frac{P_2}{P_1} \tag{37}$$

(Note that equation 37 may be obtained from equation 36 by replacing V_2 by nRT_2/P_2 and V_1 by nRT_1/P_1.)

25. Show that equations 36 and 37 for an adiabatic, reversible expansion of an ideal gas can be put into the following forms:

 a. $TV^{R/C_V} = $ constant, or $T_1/T_2 = (V_2/V_1)^{R/C_V}$

 b. $PV^\gamma = $ constant, or $P_1/P_2 = (V_2/V_1)^\gamma$, where $\gamma = C_P/C_V$.

26. An increase of entropy may correspond to an increase of randomness of velocities, or momenta, rather than of positions. For example, when a gas is heated at constant volume there can be no change in the spatial disorder but there is more of a spread in the molecular speeds. What conclusions can be drawn concerning the change in temperature when an isolated supersaturated solution spontaneously separates into two phases by precipitation of solute?

3

Physical Equilibria

The power of thermodynamics lies in its applicability to all substances in all states. It is not limited to such abstractions as ideal gases, ideal solutions, or perfect crystals, although certain of the equations take on especially simple forms for such special cases. In the following discussions of physical equilibria and chemical equilibria the exact thermodynamic equations will be derived wherever possible. This will enable a rational choice of approximations for each application and a clearer understanding of when, and what, approximations are being introduced.

General Conditions for Equilibrium

The fundamental requirement for a system to be at equilibrium, with respect to a certain process, is that under the existing conditions the process should be thermodynamically reversible. The requirement is, from the second law, that the entropy of the system and the surroundings should remain unchanged for small changes in the state of the system. This is a basic statement, from which other conditions can be derived. It is not, however, the most useful way of stating the conditions of equilibrium. In this chapter the conditions for equilibrium not involving chemical change will be

49

put into a variety of forms. Depending upon the process considered, one or another of these will be found most convenient.

CONDITIONS OF TEMPERATURE, PRESSURE, AND FREE ENERGY.   It was shown in the previous chapter that the second law requires that two bodies in equilibrium should have the same temperature and the same pressure. It will therefore be assumed in the following discussion that these conditions are satisfied. We will be interested in the question of what that temperature and pressure must be, and how these parameters are affected by each other and by changes in chemical composition.

It was also shown that a necessary and sufficient condition for equilibrium at constant temperature and pressure is that the free energy be a minimum, and hence that the free-energy change of the system be zero for small changes in the system. This condition will form the basis of the derivations in this chapter.

CLAPEYRON EQUATION.   Pure water freezes at $0°C$ and boils at $100°C$, but only under "normal" conditions, of 1 atm pressure. An increase of pressure will lower the freezing point but will raise the boiling point. Both effects are easily predicted by the Clapeyron equation, which is to be developed.

Let some substance exist in two phases, A and B, in equilibrium at some temperature and pressure. This might be the equilibrium between ice and liquid water, or liquid water and its vapor, or some other solid-solid, solid-liquid, solid-vapor, or liquid-vapor equilibrium. Then the condition for equilibrium is

$$\Delta G = G_B - G_A = 0 \tag{1}$$

We change the temperature and simultaneously change the pressure in such a way that equilibrium is maintained. This requires that G_A and G_B change by the same amount.

$$dG_A = dG_B \tag{2}$$

From equations 21, 22, and 23 in Chapter 2, the change in free energy with temperature and pressure is

$$dG_B = V_B \, dP - S_B \, dT$$
$$dG_A = V_A \, dP - S_A \, dT$$

and therefore

$$V_B \, dP - S_B \, dT = V_A \, dP - S_A \, dT$$

This can be rearranged to give

(Equil. between two phases) $$\frac{dP}{dT} = \frac{S_B - S_A}{V_B - V_A} = \frac{\Delta S}{\Delta V} \tag{3}$$

Because equilibrium is maintained, $\Delta G = 0$ and $\Delta S = \Delta H/T$. This gives the Clapeyron equation in its usual form:

(Equil. between two phases)
$$\frac{dP}{dT} = \frac{\Delta H}{T\,\Delta V} \qquad (4)$$

From this equation the change in a freezing point, or other phase transition, with change of applied pressure can be calculated.

For example, the freezing point of water under 1 atm of air is exactly $0°C$. The freezing point under 20 atm pressure can be calculated as follows.[1]

$$\frac{\Delta P}{\Delta T} = \frac{19 \text{ atm}}{\Delta T} = \frac{\Delta H}{T\,\Delta V} = \frac{-80 \text{ cal/gm}}{273 \text{ deg} \times 0.09 \text{ ml/gm}} \times \frac{82 \text{ ml-atm}}{2 \text{ cal}}$$

$$\Delta T = \frac{-19 \times 273 \times 0.09 \times 2}{80 \times 82} \text{ deg} = -0.14°C$$

Escaping Tendency

The thermodynamic picture of equilibrium is static, with no tendency for change in the total amounts of material in the two phases. The molecular picture of equilibrium is dynamic, with molecules continually passing back and forth from one phase to the other; but this dynamic model is entirely consistent with the static concept of equilibrium because the number of molecules passing in one direction is just equal, at equilibrium, to the number of molecules passing in the other direction.

Employing either the macroscopic and static picture or the dynamic molecular view, we may say that at equilibrium the tendency for molecules, or material, to "escape" from one phase to the other is the same as the tendency for molecules, or material, to "escape" in the reverse direction. In this language, the condition for equilibrium is that *the escaping tendency for any substance must be the same in all phases in equilibrium.*

The free energy is a measure of this escaping tendency. The higher the free energy, the greater the escaping tendency and the lower the stability of a phase. The minimum free energy, or minimum escaping tendency, represents the most stable, or equilibrium, condition. The free energy itself is not convenient for many problems, however. First, we cannot know an absolute value for the free energy, but only values relative to arbitrary standard states. Second, if some arbitrary value is assigned for a certain standard state, the value of G will become negative and infinite as the pressure of a gas or concentration of a solute approach zero. Gases at low pressures, and dilute solutions, are too important to permit such awkward

---

[1] The substitution of $\Delta P/\Delta T$ for dP/dT is justified because the change in temperature is small. More generally, one could carry out the integration to obtain $\int dP = \Delta P = \frac{\Delta H}{\Delta V}$ $\int \frac{dT}{T} = \frac{\Delta H}{\Delta V} \ln \frac{T_2}{T_1}$. However, $\ln T_2/T_1 = \ln\left(1 + \frac{T_2 - T_1}{T_1}\right)$ and for small values of x, $\ln(1 + x) = x$. Therefore, for $(T_2 - T_1)/T_1$ small, $\Delta P = \frac{\Delta H}{\Delta V}\frac{\Delta T}{T_1}$ or $\frac{\Delta P}{\Delta T} = \frac{\Delta H}{T\,\Delta V}$.

behavior of the function used to describe them. We turn, therefore, for this purpose to the vapor pressure or to an idealization of the vapor pressure.

VAPOR PRESSURE AND CLAUSIUS-CLAPEYRON EQUATION.   At room temperature (25°C) water molecules will leave the surface of the liquid at a rate that is just equal to the rate at which molecules of the vapor strike the surface, if the vapor is also at room temperature and at a pressure of 23.756 torr[2]; that is, at 100% relative humidity. If the temperature is raised the molecules in the liquid will have higher speeds and more of them will escape from the surface. The molecules in the vapor will also have higher speeds and more of them will strike the surface, even at the pressure of 23.756 torr. Is this enough to maintain equilibrium? It is not, for the following reason.

The number of molecules escaping from the surface depends on the number having speeds above some limiting value. The number of molecules having speeds above a limiting energy value depends exponentially on the temperature. The increase in average speed in the vapor depends only on the square root of temperature. Therefore, in order to maintain equilibrium, the density of molecules, or the pressure, must be increased, and in fact it must increase exponentially.

An approximate equation describing the change of vapor pressure with temperature can be derived from the Clapeyron equation by assuming the vapor to be an ideal gas. The volume of one mole of the vapor is RT/P and the volume of the liquid is negligible in comparison so RT/P may be taken as ΔV. Thus

$$\frac{dP}{dT} = \frac{\Delta H}{T}\frac{P}{RT}$$

or

(Ideal vapor in equil. with liquid or solid) $\frac{dP}{P\,dT} = \frac{d\ln P}{dT} = \frac{\Delta H}{RT^2}$ (5)

This is called the *Clausius-Clapeyron equation.* It serves for calculations of changes of boiling point, or sublimation point, with change of pressure, which is equivalent to saying that it gives the variation of the vapor pressure of a solid or liquid with change in temperature. It is only an approximation, since vapors at their condensation points are not ideal gases, but it is often a suitably good approximation.

The percentage change in vapor pressure, $\Delta P/P$, for a one-degree change in temperature for water at its normal boiling point, can be found from the Clausius-Clapeyron equation. The heat of vaporization of water is 540 cal/gm or 9720 cal/mole, at 100°C. Therefore,

$$\frac{\Delta P}{P} = \frac{9720 \text{ cal/mole} \times 1 \text{ deg}}{2 \text{ cal/mole-deg} \times (373)^2 \text{ deg}^2} = 0.035 = 3.5\%$$

For larger changes of temperature the differential form of the Clausius-

[2] 1 torr = 1 "mm of Hg"; see p. 28.

Clapeyron equation (equation 5) must be integrated to give the equation

$$\ln \frac{P_2}{P_1} = \frac{\Delta H \, \Delta T}{RT_1 T_2} \tag{6}$$

This form assumes that the heat of vaporization (or heat of sublimation) is a constant over the temperature range $\Delta T = T_2 - T_1$. It should be recognized that ΔH does depend on temperature, because the heat capacities of condensed phase and gas phase are different. The change in ΔH is, however, usually small compared to ΔH itself if ΔT is small, and the error can be further reduced by substitution of an average value for ΔH into equation 6.

From equation 6 the vapor pressure of water at room temperature would be calculated as follows:

$$\ln \frac{P_2}{760} = \frac{540 \times 18(-75)}{2 \times 298 \times 373} = -3.28$$

$$P_2 = 760/26.6 = 28.6 \text{ torr}$$

Substitution of an average value for ΔH of about 560 cal/gm would change the final answer to $P_2 = 25.2$ torr. The experimental value is 23.756 torr. Over a smaller temperature range better agreement would be expected.

The pressure appearing in the Clausius-Clapeyron equation is the pressure of the (ideal) pure vapor in equilibrium with the liquid. It is not necessarily the same as the total pressure applied to the liquid. For example, the pressure on water in the laboratory is 1 atm, applied by the air, but the pressure of the water vapor at equilibrium is only 23.756 torr, or about 0.03 atm. The pressure of a single component is often called the "partial pressure," to distinguish it from the total pressure. It is the equilibrium partial pressure, or vapor pressure, that is a measure of the escaping tendency of the liquid. The escaping tendency of the liquid is affected, but only slightly, by the total applied pressure.

FUGACITY. When the vapor is ideal there is a simple, exact relationship between vapor pressure and the thermodynamic properties, especially the free energy, G (equation 28, Chapter 2). It would be a great help to have an exact relationship for real gases and the escaping tendencies of liquids and solids that could be employed for thermodynamic calculations.

The logical requirement for this new function, f, is that it should coincide with the vapor pressure of a solid or liquid, and with the partial pressure of a vapor, whenever the vapor is ideal, but it should retain the same functional relationship to G even when the vapor is non-ideal. This new measure of escaping tendency may be considered a more practical vapor pressure. We define this function, f, by the **two** equations

$$\Delta G = RT \ln \frac{f_2}{f_1} \tag{7}$$

and

$$\lim_{P \to 0} \frac{f}{P} = 1 \tag{8}$$

An alternative form of the first of these equations is to write

$$G = RT \ln f + B(T) \tag{7a}$$

with the unknown function $B(T)$, depending on temperature, added so that absolute values can be assigned to f even though absolute values are not known for G. The function f is called *fugacity*, from the same Latin root (fugere) as "fugitive." The value to be inserted for G when the substance is not pure is an effective value, to be discussed later.

From the defining equations (7 and 8) a value for the fugacity can be found experimentally for any substance. At a sufficiently low pressure of the vapor it will be ideal, and fugacity will equal pressure. The change in free energy with pressure can be found from equation 22, Chapter 2,

$$\Delta G = \int V \, dP \tag{9}$$

If the volume is known for each pressure, this integral can be evaluated (by numerical integration if necessary) and the fugacity at the higher pressure can be found from the change in free energy:

$$\Delta G = \int_{P_1}^{P_2} V \, dP = RT \ln \frac{f_2}{f_1} = RT \ln \frac{f_2}{P_1} \tag{10}$$

In this equation, P_1 is chosen to be sufficiently small so that $P_1 = f_1$. Alternatively, the volume may be written

$$V = \frac{RT}{P} + \alpha$$

where α is a correction term that varies with pressure and is zero for zero pressure. Then, for any P_1 and P_2,

$$\Delta G = RT \ln \frac{P_2}{P_1} + \int_{P_1}^{P_2} \alpha \, dP \tag{10a}$$

In practice these somewhat tedious integrations are seldom necessary.

Fugacity tables are available for gases. When the actual volume of a gas is known at a certain temperature and pressure, the fugacity may be approximated by means of the equation

$$f \approx P^2 V / RT$$

or, letting $P_i = RT/V$,

$$\frac{f}{P} \approx \frac{P}{P_i} \tag{11}$$

This equation can be derived from van der Waals' equation or other similar equations of state by neglecting second-order correction terms. Note that the fugacity differs from the true pressure of a non-ideal gas in the opposite direction from that of the "ideal" pressure, $P_i = RT/V$.

In many applications we need not know the absolute value of the fugacity but only a relative value compared to some standard state. The ratio, $f/f°$, where $f°$ is the fugacity in the particular standard state chosen, is called the *activity*. The activity is a dimensionless ratio; the value of the ratio depends on the choice of standard state as well as the state of the substance being described. Different standard states are frequently employed in different problems, or often even in the same problem, so different values of the activity are obtained for a given state of any substance.

In the discussions that follow the reader may, without appreciable error, substitute the term "vapor pressure" for fugacity, or else the term "partial pressure" if the substance is itself a vapor. The equations are exactly true as given and are approximately true if vapor pressures (or partial pressures) are used as approximations to the fugacity. (Note, however, that the total applied pressure may be very different from the vapor pressure, or fugacity, of a solid or liquid.)

EXACT CLAUSIUS-CLAPEYRON EQUATION.   The Clapeyron equation (equation 4) is an exact expression relating total applied pressure to the temperature. From it an approximate equation (equation 5), the Clausius-Clapeyron equation, was derived by assuming the vapor to be ideal and by neglecting the volume of the condensed phase. It is now possible to derive an exact form of the Clausius-Clapeyron equation, which will prove invaluable in later applications where the assumptions of ideal vapors will be unnecessary or inappropriate.

Fugacity is a measure of tendency to escape and we wish to consider the process of escape of molecules from a condensed phase into the vapor phase at a sufficiently low pressure that interactions in the vapor are negligible. Thus we take as the "escaped" state a pressure, P^*, sufficiently low that $f^* = P^*$. If H^* is the enthalpy of the vapor at such a low pressure and H is the enthalpy of the substance (at the equilibrium pressure) in the condensed phase (liquid or solid) the Clausius-Clapeyron equation may be written in the exact form

(Vapor in equil. with liquid or solid) $$\frac{d \ln f}{dT} = \frac{H^* - H}{RT^2} \qquad (12)$$

The enthalpy difference, $H^* - H$, is the heat of vaporization (or the heat of sublimation) plus a small correction term for the change of pressure from the equilibrium pressure to the very low pressure.

$$H^* - H = \Delta H_{vap} + \int_P^{P^*} \left(\frac{\partial H}{\partial P}\right)_T dP \qquad (13)$$

The second term, the variation of enthalpy of the vapor with pressure, is sufficiently small that it can usually be neglected; for an ideal gas it would be identically zero. Also, for an ideal gas the fugacity is equal to the vapor pressure, so for an ideal gas, equation 12 becomes identical with equation 5.

The exact Clausius-Clapeyron equation may be derived as follows. The free-energy change in going from the condensed phase, at some pressure P, to the vapor at the very low pressure P^* is

$$\Delta G = G^* - G = RT \ln \frac{f^*}{f}$$

(For the vaporization step there is no change in free energy, or fugacity, but there is a change in free energy with change of pressure.) This is easily rearranged to give

$$\ln f = \frac{G - G^*}{RT} + \ln f^*$$

To find the temperature dependence we take the derivative with respect to temperature (with pressure constant and maintaining equilibrium between the two phases):

$$\frac{d \ln f}{dT} = (G - G^*) \frac{d}{dT}\left(\frac{1}{RT}\right) + \frac{1}{RT} \frac{d}{dT}(G - G^*) + \frac{d \ln f^*}{dT}$$

The last term is zero, because $f^* = P^*$ was chosen as an arbitrary but fixed value, independent of temperature. Employing equation 23, Chapter 2, the remaining terms give

$$\frac{d \ln f}{dT} = \frac{G^* - G}{RT^2} + \frac{S^* - S}{RT}$$

$$= \frac{H^* - H}{RT^2}$$

Colligative Properties; Laws of Dilute Solutions

The liquid phase is the most difficult to understand and to describe quantitatively. The molecules cannot be considered independent of each other, as in a gas, nor are they arranged in a regular, fixed structure, as in a crystal. There is great individuality of behavior of pure liquids, and of solutions, so that few generalizations can be made.

The one area in which thermodynamics has been most extensively and successfully applied is that of very dilute solutions. The laws that can be derived for very dilute solutions are largely independent of the nature of the solute molecules but depend on the number of such solute molecules. They are called "colligative" (meaning collective) properties. The dilute-solution laws are commonly applied to solutions of moderate or even high concentrations, much as the ideal-gas law is applied to real gases as an approximation. Indeed, just as the ideal-gas laws were suggested by measurements on real gases, the dilute-solution laws were suggested by measurements on non-dilute solutions. However, the errors encountered in extrapolation of the equations to moderate or high concentrations can be quite large. It is best to remember that these equations **must** hold for infinitely dilute solutions and **may** hold for greater concentrations.

In the following derivations and formulas it will be convenient to call the major constituent the solvent and designate it by the subscript 1; minor constituents will be called solutes and designated by subscripts 2, 3, etc. Concentrations will be expressed as mole fractions or, later, as molarity or molality. The mole fraction of any component in a mixture is the number of moles of that component divided by the sum of the number of moles of all components. Letting n_1, n_2, ... represent the number of moles of components 1, 2, etc., the mole fraction, N_i, of the ith component is

$$N_i = \frac{n_i}{n_1 + n_2 + \cdots}$$

The symbol X_i is also sometimes employed for the mole fraction. Molarity is the concentration expressed as moles of solute per liter (or 1000 cm^3) of solution. For example, 0.3 mole of NaCl in sufficient water to give one liter of solution gives a "0.3 molar" solution, written 0.3 M. Molality is the concentration expressed as moles of solute per kilogram of solvent. Thus 0.3 mole of NaCl in 1 kg of H_2O gives a "0.3 molal" solution, written 0.3 m. For dilute water solutions molarity and molality are nearly the same, but for concentrated water solutions or, especially, solutions in other solvents the molarity and molality may be very different.

DILUTE-SOLUTION POSTULATE.   The laws of dilute solutions rely on a single postulate, which has been demonstrated to have wide validity for solutes that do not dissociate upon dilution. Thus the following equations apply to sugar or to Na$^+$ ions and Cl$^-$ ions (because NaCl is fully dissociated at moderate concentrations) in water, or to solutions of polymeric materials, such as polystyrene, even though these may have molecular weights of hundreds of thousands. The range of validity—that is, what constitutes a very dilute solution—will differ from one solute to another, so some understanding is required in judging the accuracy of the dilute-solution laws in particular examples. The methods of statistical mechanics show that the condition to be satisfied is that solute-solute interactions should be negligible as compared with solute-solvent and solvent-solvent interactions. When the solute does dissociate upon dilution, as does acetic acid, the dilute-solution laws can be applied to the dissociation products. In practice it is often adequate to consider the solute to be a mixture of undissociated and dissociated solute and treat these as different solutes.

If the fugacity of a solute is plotted against concentration it is obvious that the fugacity (or vapor pressure) of the solute must decrease to zero as the concentration of the solute decreases to zero. There are, in principle, three possibilities, as shown in Figure 1. The slope at the origin might be infinite, or zero, or have some finite, non-zero value. On the basis of many experimental measurements the following statement is put forth as a postulate: *For all solutes that do not dissociate upon dilution, the slope of fugacity against concentration, df/dN_2, at the origin is finite and non-zero.*

HENRY'S LAW.   In 1803 William Henry proposed, on the basis of his measurements, that *the solubility of a gas in a liquid increases in proportion*

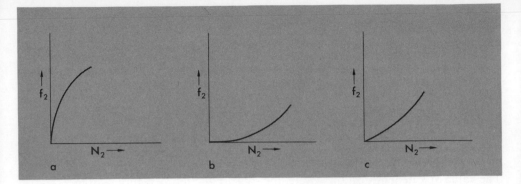

FIGURE 1 *When fugacity of a solute is plotted against concentration of the solute, the slope at the origin could be (a) infinite, (b) zero, or (c) finite and non-zero. Experiments have shown that such slopes are finite and non-zero, as shown in (c).*

to the pressure of the gas. This result can be easily derived from the dilute-solution postulate, which can be written

$$\left.\frac{df_2}{dN_2}\right)_{N_2 \to 0} = k \tag{14}$$

The number k is the value of the slope at the origin, which will depend on the solute and on the solvent, and the notation $N_2 \to 0$ will be used to indicate that the solution is very dilute. (That is, as N_2 approaches zero the equation must become valid.) A derivative is, by definition, the limiting value for the ratio of the changes in the dependent and independent variable, or, in this case, the limiting value, as ΔN_2 is made small, of the ratio $\Delta f_2/\Delta N_2$. But Δf_2 can be written $f_2 - 0$, for a small increment of fugacity at the origin, and ΔN_2 can similarly be written $N_2 - 0$. With these substitutions we write

$$\left.\frac{df_2}{dN_2}\right)_{N_2 \to 0} = \left.\frac{\Delta f_2}{\Delta N_2}\right)_{N_2 \to 0} = \left.\frac{f_2 - 0}{N_2 - 0}\right)_{N_2 \to 0} = \left.\frac{f_2}{N_2}\right)_{N_2 \to 0}$$

Combining this result with equation 14, we obtain

$$(N_2 \to 0) \qquad\qquad \frac{f_2}{N_2} = k$$

or

$$(N_2 \to 0) \qquad\qquad f_2 = kN_2 \tag{15}$$

For a very dilute solution the fugacity, and vapor pressure, of the solute are very small and therefore the fugacity is equal to the vapor pressure:

$$(N_2 \to 0) \qquad\qquad P_2 = kN_2 \tag{15a}$$

This is *Henry's law.* For dilute solutions the concentration, c_2, expressed as

58

molarity or molality, is proportional to the mole fraction, N_2, so Henry's law may be written in the more general form

$$(c_2 \to 0) \qquad\qquad f_2 = kc_2 \qquad\qquad\qquad (15b)$$

or

$$(c_2 \to 0) \qquad\qquad P_2 = kc_2 \qquad\qquad\qquad (15c)$$

The value of k depends on the solute, the solvent, the temperature, and the units in which c_2 is expressed (mole fraction, molarity, or molality) and the units in which f_2 or P_2 is expressed (usually atm or torr). Small deviations from equation 15c may be observed at moderate concentrations because the vapor is not ideal; large deviations may occur because the solution may not obey equation 15b (or 15) in solutions that are not highly dilute.

An example of Henry's law is provided by the human respiratory circulatory system. Blood entering the lungs is exposed to air containing approximately 0.20 atm oxygen, and it becomes saturated, at this pressure, with oxygen. Because when the blood reaches the capillaries the pressure of oxygen in the surrounding tissues is less than 0.20 atm, oxygen is given up by the blood to the surrounding tissues. At the same time, the blood picks up carbon dioxide at the comparatively high pressure of the tissues surrounding the capillaries and loses carbon dioxide in the lungs where the partial pressure of the CO_2 is comparatively low. Although both gases are bound chemically within the blood (with hemoglobin or as carbonates), the release or pickup of the gas is controlled by the fugacity of the free gas in the liquid phase, which is controlled, through Henry's law, by the partial pressure of the gas in the surrounding medium (the air of the lungs or the fluids around the capillaries).

NERNST'S DISTRIBUTION LAW.   When two solutions, containing the same solute but different, immiscible solvents, are brought to equilibrium, the final concentration of the solute will generally be higher in one solvent than in the other. However, the *ratio* of the concentrations remains unchanged if more solute is added, provided the solutions are dilute.

Consider one solute distributed between two immiscible solvents, A and B (Figure 2). The concentration of the solute in solvent A is c_2^A and the concentration of the same solute in solvent B is c_2^B. From Henry's law,

FIGURE 2   *A certain solute has a concentration c_2^A in solvent A and a concentration c_2^B in solvent B. The solvents are immiscible and the solutions are in equilibrium.*

$$(c_2^A \to 0) \qquad f_2^A = k_A c_2^A$$
$$(c_2^B \to 0) \qquad f_2^B = k_B c_2^B$$

In order that the system be at equilibrium, the free energy of the solute must be the same in the two solutions. This requires that the fugacity of the solute be the same,

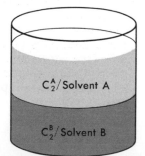

c_2^A/Solvent A

c_2^B/Solvent B

$$f_2{}^A = f_2{}^B$$

and therefore

$$k_A c_2{}^A = k_B c_2{}^B$$

or

$$(c_2{}^A \to 0,\ c_2{}^B \to 0) \qquad \frac{c_2{}^A}{c_2{}^B} = \frac{k_B}{k_A} = K_D \tag{16}$$

The ratio of the two Henry's law constants, k_B/k_A, is also a constant, which is known as the *distribution constant,* or *distribution coefficient, K_D. Nernst's distribution law* states that *for dilute solutions a solute will divide itself between two immiscible solvents to give a constant ratio of concentrations* (over a range of concentrations for which k_A and k_B are constant).

The distribution law is the basis of solvent extraction procedures. Distribution coefficients are also important, for example, in the storage of gasoline, which is a mixture of many hydrocarbons. The storage tanks must be vented to the air and consequently water vapor can condense in the tanks. The water is not significantly soluble and simply sinks to the bottom of the tank, where it might be expected to cause no trouble. However, the blending of gasolines, especially for winter driving, requires a carefully controlled percentage of the lighter hydrocarbons, such as butane and pentane. Because these hydrocarbons are more soluble than the heavier hydrocarbons in water, the water layer becomes richer in light hydrocarbons and the gasoline becomes slightly depleted in the lighter, more volatile compounds. The effect is to make the gasoline poor in cold-weather starting properties if the fractionation is not properly compensated for.

IDEAL SOLUTIONS. Henry's law states that, *over the concentration range for which it is valid, the fugacity, or vapor pressure, of a solute is proportional to the concentration of that solute.* The proportionality constant for each solute-solvent system must be determined by experiment.

In certain solutions the Henry's law constant takes on a particular value —the value of the fugacity, or vapor pressure, of the pure component— when the concentration is expressed as a mole fraction. Then, for the ith component,

$$f_i = f_i{}^\circ N_i \tag{17}$$

A solution for which each component obeys equation 17 is called an *ideal solution,* and equation 17 is called *Raoult's law.* It will be shown later that Raoult's law will necessarily apply for the solvent (the major component) when a solution is very dilute, just as Henry's law must then apply to the solute (the minor component).

One of the properties of an ideal solution is that there is no heat effect upon mixing the components. Another property is that the volumes are additive.

(I. Soln.) $\qquad V_{A+B} = V_A + V_B$

Let v_A and v_B represent molar volumes of liquids A and B, and let V represent the volume of the solution of A and B. Then, for an ideal solution comprising n_A moles of A and n_B moles of B,

(I. Soln.) $$V = n_A v_A + n_B v_B \tag{18}$$

PARTIAL MOLAL QUANTITIES.   It would very often be convenient to have an equation, for non-ideal solutions, similar to equation 18, by which the total volume could be ascribed to the "effective" contributions of the two components. These effective molar volumes will be indicated by $\overline{V}_A$ and $\overline{V}_B$. Then

$$V = n_A \overline{V}_A + n_B \overline{V}_B \tag{19}$$

for any solution of two components, A and B, whether the solution is ideal or not. The equation is easily extended to any number of components.

If the number of moles of A is held constant and more B is added to the solution, how much will the total volume increase? Assume $\overline{V}_A$ and $\overline{V}_B$ are not significantly changed.[3] Then

$$dV = d(n_A \overline{V}_A) + d(n_B \overline{V}_B)$$

but since n_A is constant,

(n_A) $\qquad dV = \overline{V}_B \, dn_B$

or

$$\left.\frac{\partial V}{\partial n_B}\right)_{n_A} = \overline{V}_B \tag{20}$$

This equation serves to define the effective molar volume. It is a partial derivative, since n_A is held constant, and is commonly called the *partial molal volume,* or sometimes the *partial molar volume.* A graphical interpretation of the partial molal volume is that it is the slope of the plot of total volume against moles of the component added, at constant temperature and pressure, with the amounts of all other components held fixed (Figure 3).

The same arguments can be applied to any extensive properties of a solution: G, H, C_P, etc. The quantity of primary

FIGURE 3   *The partial molal volume, V_i, is the slope of the curve when the volume of a solution is plotted against the number of moles of the ith component, the amounts of other components remaining constant.*

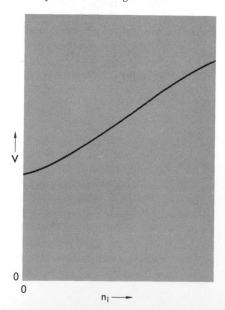

[3] It will be shown later that even this restriction is not important, since the changes would be compensating.

interest here is the partial molal free energy. For the ith component of a solution,

$$\overline{G}_i = \frac{\partial G}{\partial n_i}\Bigg)_{T,P,n} \tag{21}$$

This definition shows that the effective free energy per mole of the ith component is the rate of change of the total free energy of the solution upon addition of a small additional amount of the ith component, holding temperature, pressure, and the amounts of all other substances constant. As in equation 19, one can write, for any solution,

$$G = n_1\overline{G}_1 + n_2\overline{G}_2 + n_3\overline{G}_3 + \cdots \tag{22}$$

This equation is particularly important since the free energy of a solution is not the sum of the free energies of the pure components, even for an ideal solution. There is, upon mixing, an entropy increase that is reflected in a decrease of free energy. The partial molal free energies differ from the molal free energies of the pure components by correction terms for the entropy of mixing and the heat of mixing. It is most convenient, therefore, to employ the partial molal free energy, or the "effective free energy per mole," in all equations. For a pure substance the partial molal free energy is identical with the molal free energy.

The significance of the partial molal free energy in chemical thermodynamics cannot be overemphasized; it is the necessary key to the treatment of all solutions, whether solid, liquid, or gaseous. And, since it includes pure materials as a special case, it provides a single function for the thermodynamic treatment of all substances. A necessary condition for physical equilibrium is that, for **each** substance, the partial molal free energy must be the same in every phase. Furthermore, chemical reactions can occur only in a manner that will minimize the total free energy (for the isothermal process), which is a sum of partial molal free energies, each multiplied by the number of moles (equation 22). Thus $\overline{G}_i$ is a measure of the potential reactivity of the ith species. Because of this particular importance, the partial molal free energy is often called the *chemical potential*, and given the symbol μ_i.

$$\overline{G}_i = \mu_i$$

The free energy of a solution depends upon the number of moles of each of the constituents, on the temperature, and on the pressure. Therefore the change in free energy arising from changes in any of these quantities can be written as the sum

$$dG = \frac{\partial G}{\partial n_1}\Bigg) dn_1 + \frac{\partial G}{\partial n_2}\Bigg) dn_2 + \frac{\partial G}{\partial n_3}\Bigg) dn_3 + \cdots + \frac{\partial G}{\partial P}\Bigg) dP + \frac{\partial G}{\partial T}\Bigg) dT$$

It is to be understood that each of these partial derivatives is evaluated with the other variables held constant. Substitution of equation 21 and of equations 22 and 23 of Chapter 2 puts this equation into the form

$$dG = \overline{G}_1 \, dn_1 + \overline{G}_2 \, dn_2 + \overline{G}_3 \, dn_3 + \cdots + V \, dP - S \, dT \qquad (23)$$

This is a more general form of equation 21, Chapter 2.

Equation 22 is a completely general equation and it can be differentiated, term by term, to give

$$dG = \overline{G}_1 \, dn_1 + n_1 \, d\overline{G}_1 + \overline{G}_2 \, dn_2 + n_2 \, d\overline{G}_2 + \overline{G}_3 \, dn_3 + n_3 \, d\overline{G}_3 + \cdots \qquad (24)$$

Subtraction of equation 23 from equation 24 gives the *Gibbs-Duhem equation*

$$0 = n_1 \, d\overline{G}_1 + n_2 \, d\overline{G}_2 + n_3 \, d\overline{G}_3 + \cdots - V \, dP + S \, dT \qquad (25)$$

which relates the changes in partial molal free energies to changes of the amount of any constituent, changes of temperature, or changes of pressure —all evaluated, of course, at some particular concentration, temperature, and pressure. An important variation of this equation is obtained by assuming constant temperature and pressure:

$$(T, P) \qquad n_1 \, d\overline{G}_1 + n_2 \, d\overline{G}_2 + n_3 \, d\overline{G}_3 + \cdots = 0 \qquad (25a)$$

Thus the additional terms that appear in equation 24, beyond those of equation 23, add up to zero. (It may be noted that an equation similar to equation 25a must hold for partial molal volumes, which justifies ignoring changes in $\overline{V}_A$ and $\overline{V}_B$ in proceeding to equation 20, by which the partial molal volumes were subsequently defined.)

RAOULT'S LAW. The addition of a small amount of solute to any solvent will, of course, increase (from zero) the vapor pressure of the solute. It will also decrease the vapor pressure of the solvent below the value for the pure solvent. The solute vapor pressure is given by Henry's law (equation 15); the solvent vapor pressure is given by Raoult's law, which says that the vapor pressure of the solvent is proportional to the mole fraction of the solvent.

From equation 25 we can derive the relationship between the fugacity or vapor pressure of the solvent and the composition of the solution. Substitution of equation 7a into equation 25a gives, for three components,

$$n_1 \, d \ln f_1 + n_2 \, d \ln f_2 + n_3 \, d \ln f_3 = 0$$

Dividing by $n_1 + n_2 + n_3$ gives

$$(T, P) \qquad N_1 \, d \ln f_1 + N_2 \, d \ln f_2 + N_3 \, d \ln f_3 = 0 \qquad (26)$$

For N_2 and N_3 very small, equation 15 requires that $f_2/N_2 = df_2/dN_2$. Therefore,

$$(N_2 \to 0) \qquad N_2 \, d \ln f_2 = N_2 \frac{df_2}{f_2} = N_2 \frac{dN_2}{N_2} = dN_2 \qquad (27)$$

and similarly for the third component. Therefore,

$$(N_2 \to 0, N_3 \to 0) \qquad N_1 \, d \ln f_1 + dN_2 + dN_3 = 0 \qquad (28)$$

and integration from pure solvent $(N_2 = N_3 = 0)$ to dilute solution $(N_2$ and N_3 very small) gives[4]

$$N_1 \ln \frac{f_1}{f_1{}^\circ} + N_2 + N_3 = 0$$

The logarithm can be expanded by means of the approximation

$$\ln (1 - x) = -x$$

for $x \ll 1$.

$$\ln \frac{f_1}{f_1{}^\circ} = \ln \left(1 - \frac{f_1{}^\circ - f_1}{f_1{}^\circ}\right) = -\frac{f_1{}^\circ - f_1}{f_1{}^\circ}$$

With this substitution,

$$N_1 f_1 - N_1 f_1{}^\circ + N_2 f_1{}^\circ + N_3 f_1{}^\circ = 0$$

Divide by N_1 and rearrange, writing N_2 for N_2/N_1 and N_3 for N_3/N_1 because N_1 is practically one in the dilute solution. (This approximation, like others in the derivation, ignores terms of the order of $N_2{}^2$.)

$$f_1 = f_1{}^\circ (1 - N_2 - N_3)$$

The sum of the mole fractions is, from the definition, 1. Therefore,

$$(N_1 \to 1) \qquad\qquad f_1 = f_1{}^\circ N_1 \qquad\qquad (29)$$

This is Raoult's law, which must apply for the solvent in a very dilute solution. It gives the fugacity of the solvent, in the solution, in terms of the fugacity of the pure solvent, $f_1{}^\circ$, at the same temperature and pressure. The notation $(N_1 \to 1)$ at the left means that the equation is valid when N_1 is very nearly equal to 1, just as the notation $(N_2 \to 0)$ means N_2 has been required to be very nearly equal to zero.

Raoult's law applies for nearly pure liquids, for which the vapor pressure is not necessarily small and therefore the fugacity is not in general exactly equal to the vapor pressure. However, the ratio of the fugacities will be equal to the ratio of vapor pressures when $f_1 \approx f_1{}^\circ$ and $P_1 \approx P_1{}^\circ$.

$$\frac{f_1}{f_1{}^\circ} = \frac{P_1}{P_1{}^\circ}$$

Thus Raoult's law may be written in the more common form,

---

[4] N_1 may be considered as constant during the integration, since it is always nearly 1. Alternatively, equation 28 may be expressed in terms of n_1, n_2, and n_3 and the integrated equation divided by N_1 to give the same result.

$$(N_1 \to 1) \qquad\qquad P_1 = P_1{}^\circ N_1 \qquad\qquad (29a)$$

An ideal solution is defined as one in which all components obey Raoult's law at all concentrations.

$$\text{(I. Soln.)} \qquad\qquad f_i = f_i{}^\circ N_i \qquad\qquad (29b)$$

Because f_i and $f_i{}^\circ$ may be quite different, $f_i/f_i{}^\circ$ may be quite different from $P_i/P_i{}^\circ$. That is, the non-ideality correction for the vapor may be quite different at different values of the pressure of the gas (P_i vs. $P_i{}^\circ$). If the vapors can be assumed to be ideal, then

$$\text{(I. Soln., Ideal Vapors)} \qquad P_i = P_i{}^\circ N_i \qquad\qquad (29c)$$

From equation 29b it follows that an ideal solution also has additive volumes (equation 18) and additive enthalpies (no heat of solution).

OSMOTIC PRESSURE.   If a solution can exchange solvent with a reservoir of pure solvent, at the same temperature and pressure, solvent will necessarily pass from the pure solvent to the solution because the fugacity of the solvent in the solution, $f_1 = N_1 f_1{}^\circ$, is less than the fugacity of the pure solvent, $f_1{}^\circ$.

$$f_1 = N_1 f_1{}^\circ < f_1{}^\circ$$

No finite amount of dilution of the solution by the solvent can achieve equilibrium.

Equilibrium can, however, be reached if the fugacity, f_1, of solvent in the solution is increased by an increase of pressure on the solution (but not on the pure solvent reservoir). The additional pressure required, which may be quite large, is called the *osmotic pressure*.

One effective experimental arrangement for demonstrating osmotic pressure is shown in Figure 4. The solvent, in the beaker, passes through the membrane (called *semipermeable* because it allows the solvent molecules to pass, but not the solute molecules). This dilutes the solution in the thistle tube and forces the solution up the stem, increasing the hydrostatic pressure on the solution.

Consider a system in which there is pure

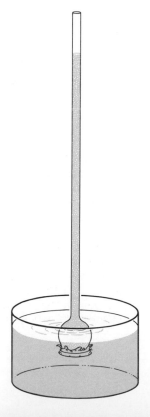

FIGURE 4   *In a typical demonstration of osmotic pressure, a solution of molasses in water is placed in a thistle tube and closed with a membrane. Water passes through the membrane, causing an increased hydrostatic pressure on the solution.*

solvent, at atmospheric pressure, on both sides of a membrane. Addition of solute to one side, to form the solution, lowers the fugacity of the solvent by dilution, but an increase of pressure on the resultant solution can increase the fugacity to its original value. The free-energy changes caused by addition of the solute and by the change of pressure will be

$$\frac{dG_1}{dn_2}\bigg)_P dn_2 + \frac{dG_1}{dP}\bigg)_{n_2} dP$$

and the sum of these terms must be zero, since the pure solvent phase is unchanged. The free-energy values should be understood to be the effective, or partial molal, free energies in these equations. Substitution of equation 7a into the first term and equation 22 of Chapter 2 into the second, using the partial molal volume of the solvent, $\overline{V}_1$, gives

$$\frac{RT\,d\ln f_1}{dN_2}\,dN_2 + \overline{V}_1\,dP = 0 \tag{30}$$

The first term is reduced with the aid of equation 28.

$$(N_2 \to 0) \qquad \frac{d\ln f_1}{dN_2}\,dN_2 = -\frac{dN_2}{N_1} = -\,dN_2 \tag{31}$$

and therefore

$$-RT\,dN_2 + \overline{V}_1\,dP = 0$$

or

$$dP = \frac{RT}{\overline{V}_1}\,dN_2$$

Integration from $N_2 = 0$ to $N_2 = N_2$ (a very small value) gives the expression for the osmotic pressure,

$$(N_2 \to 0) \qquad \Delta P = \frac{RT}{\overline{V}_1}\,N_2 \tag{32}$$

The pressure produced can be quite large, even for dilute solutions. The molar volume of water at $25°C$ is 18 ml and RT is $82.1 \times 297 = 24.4 \times 10^3$ ml-atm. Thus if N_2, the mole fraction of impurity in the water, is only 10^{-3}, the osmotic pressure is 1.35 atm or 1030 torr. The selectivity of the semipermeable membranes required for osmosis is usually based on size differences between solute and solvent molecules. The effectiveness of osmotic processes is often limited by the poor selectivity of available membranes.

Equation 32 can be easily remembered by its similarity to the ideal-gas law. $(\Delta P)\overline{V}_1 = N_2RT$ looks like $PV = nRT$. Note, however, that the volume, $\overline{V}_1$, refers to the solvent, whereas N_2 is the number of solute molecules in that volume.[5]

Osmosis may be considered to be simply a diffusion of solvent molecules

---

[5] A pseudo-derivation is as follows. If $P_1°\overline{V}_1 = N_1°RT$ for pure solvent, $P_1\overline{V}_1 = N_1RT$ for the solution, and $\overline{V}_1$ can be assumed equal for both, then $(P_1° - P_1)\overline{V}_1 = (N_1° - N_1)RT$ or $\Delta P\overline{V}_1 = N_2RT$. (But of course the ideal-gas law is not really applicable to solutions.)

from a more concentrated (in solvent) solution to a less concentrated (in solvent) solution. It is of great importance to life processes. The direction of diffusion of water can be reversed by exposure of plant or animal cells to solutions more concentrated in solute than are the cell fluids. Reverse osmosis has also been applied to the problem of producing fresh water from salt water. When the salt water is compressed beyond the osmotic pressure, water will flow through a membrane, leaving the salt behind.

CHANGE OF BOILING POINT OR FREEZING POINT.   Addition of sugar to water will raise the boiling point but lower the freezing point of the water. Addition of gasoline to water will lower the boiling point but leave the freezing point essentially unchanged. Addition of gold to silver will raise the freezing point of the silver, although addition of silver to gold lowers the freezing point of the gold. These effects, which may seem to have no consistent pattern, are all predictable by a single equation, knowing only certain properties of the pure substances and the mutual solubilities.

An impurity added to a substance at a phase transition point will usually go preferentially into one phase or the other. This lowers the fugacity of the major component in the phase that has become impure and upsets the equilibrium.

Solvent is present in both phases and it is a necessary condition for the equilibrium that the free energy of the solvent should be the same in the two phases, both before and after addition of solute. If equilibrium is re-established, after addition of solute to one phase, by changing the temperature of the two phases, the condition for final equilibrium is that the sum of concentration and temperature effects on the free energy of the solvent in the impure phase should equal the temperature effect on the free energy of the solvent in the pure phase.

$$dG_1 = dG_1°$$

Substituting fugacities (equation 7a),

$$\left(\frac{\partial \ln f_1}{\partial N_2}\right)_T dN_2 + \left(\frac{\partial \ln f_1}{\partial T}\right)_{N_2} dT = \left(\frac{\partial \ln f_1°}{\partial T}\right)_{N_2} dT$$

For example, if sugar is added to water at the boiling point, the change in fugacity of the liquid water is given by the left-hand side and the change in fugacity of the pure (that is, sugar-free) water vapor is given by the right-hand side. From equation 31 the first term is just $-dN_2$, and from the exact Clausius-Clapeyron equation (12),

$$\frac{d \ln f_1}{dT} = \frac{H_1^* - H_1}{RT^2} \quad \text{and} \quad \frac{d \ln f_1°}{dT} = \frac{H_1^* - H_1°}{RT^2}$$

in which H_1^* is the enthalpy of the solvent vapor at very low pressure, H_1 is the (partial molal) enthalpy of the solvent in the impure phase at the pressure of the equilibrium, and $H_1°$ is the (partial molal) enthalpy of the solvent in the pure phase in equilibrium with the impure phase.

Substitution of these expressions gives

$$-dN_2 + \frac{H_1^* - H_1}{RT^2} = \frac{H_1^* - H_1^\circ}{RT^2}$$

and, combining terms,

$$dN_2 = \frac{H_1^* - H_1 - (H_1^* - H_1^\circ)}{RT^2} dT$$

$$= \frac{H_1^\circ - H_1}{RT^2} dT$$

This relates the change in temperature, from the "normal" equilibrium temperature for the pure substance, to the change in mole fraction of impurity in the substance (in one phase only). Because $\Delta N_2 = N_2 - 0 = N_2$, the equation may be rewritten

$$(N_2 \to 0) \qquad\qquad N_2 = \frac{H_1^\circ - H_1}{RT^2} \Delta T \qquad\qquad (33)$$

It is clear that ΔT, which is the change in boiling point or freezing point, must have the same sign as $H_1^\circ - H_1$, which is the enthalpy change for the solvent going from the impure phase to the pure phase.[6] For example, if a solution of sugar and water is boiled, the pure phase is the water vapor and thus H_1° is the enthalpy of water vapor at the prevailing pressure; the impure phase is the liquid solution and so H_1 is the (partial molal) enthalpy of the water in the sugar solution; and $H_1^\circ - H_1$ is therefore the heat of vaporization of water, which is positive. It follows that the boiling point of a sugar-in-water solution must be higher than the boiling point of pure water, at the same pressure. If the solution of sugar and water is cooled to the freezing point, pure ice will separate out. Then the pure phase is the ice and so H_1° is the enthalpy of the ice, H_1 is the partial molal enthalpy of the water in solution, $H_1^\circ - H_1$ is the heat of freezing (-80 cal/gm), and ΔT will be negative.

If CCl_4 is mixed with water it will not dissolve, but the vapors will mix. Then N_2 will be the mole fraction of CCl_4 in the water vapor and $H_1^\circ - H_1$ will be the enthalpy of the (pure) liquid water minus the enthalpy of the water vapor; this ΔH is negative and the boiling point of the water is accordingly decreased. The boiling point of CCl_4, or of any other liquid immiscible with water, will be similarly depressed by the addition of water, a phenomenon known as *steam distillation.*

THE IMPORTANCE OF COLLIGATIVE PROPERTIES. The equations for lowering of vapor pressure of the solvent (Raoult's law), for osmotic pressure, and for change of boiling point or freezing point, share a common characteristic. Each of these expressions involves the mole fraction of the solute

---

[6] As a mnemonic device one may remember that chemists, and indeed all moral individuals, strive for greater purity. Thus ΔH is the heat absorbed in going **to** the purer phase.

or, equivalently, the mole fraction of the solvent, and is totally independent of any of the individual properties of the solute. Within the range of the dilute-solution laws, the effects calculated for any given solvent depend solely on the properties of that solvent and on the total number of molecules of solute added. There may even be a mixture of several kinds of solute molecules. The quantities measured (vapor pressure lowering, osmotic pressure, or change of boiling or freezing point) are therefore called *colligative properties.*

Measurement of a freezing point lowering, for example, will permit calculation of the number of moles of solute, so that, knowing the number of grams of solute added, an average molecular weight can be found. This is an effective means of showing whether a solute dissociates, and into how many parts. The colligative properties are also very important for determining molecular weights in polymeric materials.

The limitation to very dilute solutions is not a severe handicap in practice. Measurements can be made at several concentrations and the values extrapolated to zero concentration. The dilute-solution laws provide assurance that the extrapolation will be a straight line at the low concentration end. Also, in many applications the important question is whether the solute is or is not dimerized, or dissociated. An approximate value, at moderate concentrations, can provide the answer.

Problems

1. For the transformation of graphite to diamond at 25°C, $\Delta G = 685$ cal/mole. The densities are 2.25 and 3.51 gm/ml. What is the minimum pressure required to make diamond thermodynamically stable at this temperature?

2. At 1114°C the vapor pressure of Ni was observed to be 7.50×10^{-8} torr and at 1142°C it was 14.33×10^{-8} torr. What is the heat of vaporization of nickel in this range?

3. Is the fugacity of ice increased or decreased by exerting pressure on the ice? Which will show the greatest change in fugacity for a pressure increase of 10 atm: ice, or liquid water? Explain.

4. The vapor pressure of a liquid compound, Q, obeys the equation $\ln P = a + bT^{-1}$, with P the pressure in atm and T in °K.
   a. What is the boiling point of Q?
   b. What is the heat of vaporization at the normal boiling point?

5. Find the mole fractions of the several components if 24 gm of methane, CH_4, is mixed with 7 gm of CO, 14 gm of N_2, and 8 gm of He.

6. A saturated solution of benzoic acid, C_6H_5COOH, contains 0.32 gm in 100 gm of water. The density of the solution is 1.3 gm/ml. What is the molarity of the solution?

7. Find the mole fraction, molarity, and molality of iodine when 0.10 gm of iodine is dissolved in 100 gm of CCl_4 (density 1.59 gm/ml).

8. a. What is the molarity of water in pure water?
   b. What is the molality of water in pure water?
   c. What is the molarity of CCl_4 in pure CCl_4 (density 1.59 gm/ml)?
   d. What is the molality of CCl_4 in pure CCl_4?
   e. What is the molarity of an ideal gas at 1 atm and 25°C?

9. A solution contains, by weight, 40% water, 35% ethanol (C_2H_5OH), and 25% acetone (CH_3COCH_3).

a. Find the mole fraction of each component.
b. Find the molality of the ethanol and acetone if water is considered to be the solvent.
c. Find the molality of the water and acetone if the ethanol is considered to be the solvent.

10. The solubility of CCl_4 in water at room temperature is about 0.9 gm/L and the vapor pressure of CCl_4 is about 100 torr. What would be the equilibrium vapor pressure of CCl_4 above a beaker containing CCl_4 covered with a layer of water?

11. Water in equilibrium with air (20.9% O_2, 79.1% N_2) at $0°C$ contains 1.28×10^{-3} moles of air per liter, of which 34.91% is O_2. Calculate the Henry's law constant
    a. for O_2
    b. for N_2

12. Is the Henry's law constant for benzene in water large or small?

13. The distribution coefficient for mercuric bromide, $HgBr_2$, between water and benzene is 0.90. That is, with concentrations expressed as molarities,

$$\frac{C(HgBr_2/H_2O)}{C(HgBr_2/C_6H_6)} = 0.90.$$ An aqueous solution contains $0.010\ M\ HgBr_2$. 50 ml

of this solution is to be extracted with 150 ml of benzene.
    a. What fraction of the $HgBr_2$ is left in the aqueous phase if the extraction is made with one 150 ml portion of benzene?
    b. What fraction is left if the extraction is made with three successive 50 ml portions of benzene?

14. Over a certain range of concentrations, the volume of a solution containing m moles of NaCl in 1 kg water has been found to be, in ml,

$$V = 1002.935 + 16.670\ m + 1.636\ m^{\frac{3}{2}} + 0.170\ m^2$$

Find the partial molal volume of
    a. NaCl in a 2 m solution
    b. water in a 2 m NaCl solution
    c. pure NaCl (density 2.165 gm/ml)

15. The vapor pressures of benzene and toluene, at $27°C$, are 120 and 40 torr. Assuming an ideal solution, what is the composition of the vapor above a solution containing 100 gm of benzene (C_6H_6) and 150 gm of toluene ($C_6H_5CH_3$)?

16. In your work for Adulterated Chemicals, Inc., you have isolated a new antibiotic through a lengthy series of extractions, biological tests, and so forth. A few milligrams are available, and by the ultra-centrifuge method it has been found that the molecular weight is 10,000. It is desired to check this by another method. For a 1% by weight solution of the substance in water, calculate
    a. the freezing-point depression
    b. the boiling-point elevation
    c. the change in vapor pressure at $25°C$
    d. the osmotic pressure, at $25°C$, in cm H_2O (The density of mercury is 13.6 gm/ml.)
    Which method would you recommend?

17. Boiling occurs in a solution when the sum of the vapor pressures of the components is equal to the atmospheric pressure (or the applied pressure), but these vapor pressures are lower than for the pure materials (cf. Raoult's law, equation 29c). If two liquids are immiscible, each exhibits its own vapor pressure (in *each* phase), and "steam distillation" occurs when the sum of the vapor pressures is equal to the atmospheric pressure.
    a. Calculate the vapor pressure of pure water at $99°C$.

   b. What vapor pressure must a compound, immiscible with water, have to steam distill at 99°C when the atmospheric pressure is 745 torr?

   c. What would be the composition of the vapor in such a steam distillation?

18. A solution of 3.795 gm of sulfur in 100 gm of CS_2 boils at 46.66°C. The boiling point of pure CS_2 is 46.30°C and the heat of vaporization of CS_2 is 6400 cal/mole. From this experimental result, what is the probable formula of the sulfur molecule in the solution?

19. Show that if two phases (A and B) in equilibrium are both slightly impure, the resultant change in temperature (change in melting point or boiling point, relative to pure phases), ΔT, is given by

$$\Delta N_1 = \frac{\Delta H_1 \Delta T}{RT^2}$$

where ΔN_1 is the difference in mole fraction of the major component ($\Delta N_1 = N_1{}^A - N_1{}^B$) and ΔH_1 is the enthalpy of transition ($\Delta H_1 = \bar{H}_1{}^A - \bar{H}_1{}^B$).

4

Chemical Equilibrium

Chemical equilibrium is one of the most important applications of thermodynamics. The theory follows very simply from the equations already derived. Setting up the necessary equations in practice requires only an understanding of the meaning of a chemical equation. Most mistakes arise in the elementary process of counting the molecules or moles of reactants and products.

For some systems the solution of the mathematical equations requires some skill and, especially, some understanding of the physical implications so that reasonable assumptions and approximations can be made. For the types of problems considered here, the primary requirement is to follow a simple, methodical procedure in finding the appropriate equations, and then to insert numerical values into these equations. Solution of the equations will then be quite easy.

Free-Energy Changes in Chemical Reactions

A completely general chemical reaction may be represented in the form

$$aA + bB \longrightarrow cC + dD$$

This should be interpreted as follows: If a moles of substance A react with b moles of substance B, c moles of sub-

72

stance C and d moles of substance D may be formed. Note that there is, as yet, no concern with concentrations or amounts actually present. Also, any finite number of reactants or products could be assumed.

The free-energy change, if the reaction proceeds as written, will be

$$\Delta G = \sum_{\text{products}} n_i \overline{G}_i - \sum_{\text{reactants}} n_j \overline{G}_j$$
$$= c\overline{G}_C + d\overline{G}_D - a\overline{G}_A - b\overline{G}_B \tag{1}$$

The values of the partial molal, or effective, free energies on the right-hand side will depend upon the states of these compounds, including the temperature, the pressure, and the individual concentrations. Thus ΔG can have any value, depending upon the states of reactants and products. It should be emphasized, however, that it is assumed that the states of reactants and products are unchanged by the reaction; the temperature, pressure, and concentration of each substance is the same before and after the reaction. This can be achieved by allowing only a small fraction of the materials present to react, or by adding reactants and removing products as the reaction proceeds. If the more general problem of a chemical reaction and a change of state of reactants and/or products is to be considered, they must be treated as separate calculations.

If the reaction were to occur with all reactants and products in their standard states, the free-energy change would be the value given in tables, ΔG°.

$$\Delta G^\circ = c\overline{G}_C^\circ + d\overline{G}_D^\circ - a\overline{G}_A^\circ - b\overline{G}_B^\circ \tag{2}$$

Subtraction of equation 2 from equation 1 gives

$$\Delta G - \Delta G^\circ = c(\overline{G}_C - \overline{G}_C^\circ) + d(\overline{G}_D - \overline{G}_D^\circ) - a(\overline{G}_A - \overline{G}_A^\circ) - b(\overline{G}_B - \overline{G}_B^\circ) \tag{3}$$

At this point it is convenient to substitute the fugacities (equation 7a, Chapter 3) for the free-energy terms.

$$\overline{G}_i = RT \ln f_i + B_i(T)$$

and
$$\overline{G}_i^\circ = RT \ln f_i^\circ + B_i(T)$$

Therefore,

$$\overline{G}_i - \overline{G}_i^\circ = RT \ln \frac{f_i}{f_i^\circ} \tag{4}$$

Substitution of equation 4 into equation 3, for each of the substances, gives

$$\Delta G - \Delta G^\circ = RT\left(c \ln \frac{f_C}{f_C^\circ} + d \ln \frac{f_D}{f_D^\circ} - a \ln \frac{f_A}{f_A^\circ} - b \ln \frac{f_B}{f_B^\circ}\right)$$

The ratio of the fugacity of any substance, f_i, to the fugacity of the same substance in its standard state, $f_i°$, is called the "activity," a_i.

$$a_i = \frac{f_i}{f_i°} \tag{5}$$

Substitution of activity for the ratio of fugacities and replacement of $n \ln x$ by $\ln x^n$ gives

$$\Delta G - \Delta G° = RT(\ln a_C{}^c + \ln a_D{}^d - \ln a_A{}^a - \ln a_B{}^b)$$

which can be further simplified to the form

$$\Delta G = \Delta G° + RT \ln \frac{a_C{}^c a_D{}^d}{a_A{}^a a_B{}^b} \tag{6}$$

It will be convenient to write this in the form

$$\Delta G = \Delta G° + RT \ln Q(a) \tag{7}$$

defining $Q(a)$ to be

$$Q(a) = \frac{a_C{}^c a_D{}^d}{a_A{}^a a_B{}^b} \tag{8}$$

or the corresponding form appropriate to the particular reaction.

Equation 6 is a very important result with obvious physical interpretation. If all substances (reactants and products) are in their standard states, all activities are, by definition, equal to 1. Then $Q(a) = 1$, $\ln Q(a) = 0$, and $\Delta G = \Delta G°$. If the substances are not in their standard states, the right-hand side of equation 6 gives the correction term necessary to calculate the actual ΔG from the handbook value, $\Delta G°$. The correction term depends on the value of $Q(a)$, which depends on the individual activities and therefore on the fugacities, or on the pressure and concentration of each substance at the given temperature.

Standard States

The choice of standard states affects the value of $\Delta G°$ as it appears in tables, and determines the relationship between the state of a compound and its activity. There are certain conventions that are customarily followed, so that it is generally considered unnecessary to explain in detail the choice of standard states that has been made. Unless the conventions are understood, therefore, it may not be possible to apply thermodynamic values found in the literature. It will be observed that the choice of standard states is always such as to give a convenient form for the activity.

GASES. For an ideal gas, fugacity is equal to pressure. We choose the standard state to be 1 atm pressure. Then $f = P$, $f° = P° = 1$ atm:

$$a = \frac{f}{f°} = \frac{P_{(atm)}}{1 \text{ atm}} = |P_{(atm)}| \tag{9}$$

That is, the activity, which is a dimensionless ratio, is equal to the numerical value of the pressure, with the pressure expressed in atmospheres. This simple relationship can be extended to cover real gases by the introduction of an "activity coefficient," γ (Greek gamma), that will equal 1 if the gas is ideal, and will differ from 1 as the gas deviates from ideality.

$$a = \gamma P \tag{10}$$

The activity coefficient defined in this way has dimensions of atm^{-1}. Equation 10 is applicable to any gas, real or ideal.[1] If the gas is non-ideal it is necessary to know the value of γ.

LIQUIDS AND SOLUTIONS.   The major component of an ideal solution has a fugacity given by Raoult's law—

$$f_1 = f_1{}^\circ N_1$$

—in which $f_1{}^\circ$ is the fugacity of the pure solvent. We choose the pure solvent as the standard state so that $f_1{}^\circ$ is the fugacity in the standard state. Then

$$a_1 = \frac{f_1}{f_1{}^\circ} = N_1 \tag{11}$$

Thus the activity of the solvent is equal to its mole fraction in the ideal solution, and the activity of any pure liquid is 1. Not all solutions are ideal, so it is convenient to allow for deviations from Raoult's law by introducing an activity coefficient, as for gases, defined by the equation

$$a_1 = \gamma_1 N_1 \tag{12}$$

This activity coefficient will be dimensionless and will be 1 for a pure liquid, for a solvent in an infinitely dilute solution, or for a component of an ideal solution. It may differ appreciably from 1 when the fugacity of the liquid in solution deviates from Raoult's law.

If a solute obeys Henry's law, the fugacity will be proportional to concentration and it is possible to choose the standard state of the solute such that $f_2{}^\circ = k$, the Henry's law constant. (This may be a physically unattainable state but that is inconsequential.) Then

$$a_2 = \frac{f_2}{f_2{}^\circ} = \frac{f_2}{k} = |c_2| \tag{13}$$

with $|c_2|$ representing the numerical value of c_2. Because it is equal to the

---

[1] More generally, the standard state of any gas is taken as the ideal gas at 1 atm pressure; that is, it is a fictitious state with properties obtained from the properties of the actual gas, at sufficiently low pressures that the gas is ideal, extrapolated to 1 atm pressure using the equations for behavior of an ideal gas. The activity coefficient may then be considered as the ratio of the fugacity of the real gas to that of the idealized gas.

numerical value of the concentration, the value of the activity depends on the units chosen for expressing concentration. Common choices are molarity, molality, or sometimes mole fraction (especially when the choice between solute and solvent is ambiguous).

To allow for deviations from Henry's law we introduce, again, an activity coefficient, such that

$$a_2 = \gamma_2 c_2 \tag{14}$$

The dimensions of γ_2 will be inverse concentration; for example, if c_2 is in moles per liter, γ_2 will have units of liters per mole. Although molality has certain advantages when changes of temperature are involved, it will be assumed in subsequent discussions that the concentration of a solute is expressed as molarity. For dilute water solutions the difference between molarity and molality is negligible. Appreciable deviations from Henry's law are found for some concentrated solutions in which there are particularly strong intermolecular forces. It is such solutions that can give rise to azeotropes, for example.

Ions are treated as normal solutes, so that the activity of any ion is given by equation 14. However, large deviations from ideality occur for ions, especially those carrying multiple charges. In dilute solutions, activity coefficients of ions are less than 1, approaching 1 at infinite dilution. In concentrated solutions (on the order of $1\ M$), activity coefficients of ions may increase and become greater than 1.

The concentration of an undissociated strong electrolyte is vanishingly small. It is convenient to choose the standard state as a very low concentration such that the activity of the undissociated species (which is not normally required, anyway) will be equal to the product of activities of the ions into which it dissociates. This causes the equilibrium constant for the dissociation to be 1, and $\Delta G°$ for the dissociation to be zero. These quantities then conveniently drop out of normal calculations on solutions of ions.

SOLIDS. The fugacity of a solid is very nearly constant, at a given temperature, independent of the applied pressure. We choose this normal value of the fugacity as $f°$. The solid has an activity of 1. Appreciable deviations from unit activity for a solid may be expected under very high pressures, when impurities are present (as in the case of mercury-metal amalgams), when the solid is severely strained, or when the solid exists as extremely small particles for which surface effects cannot be neglected.

VARIATIONS AND LIMITATIONS. Other choices of standard states are possible and may be convenient for special circumstances. For example, the standard state of a gas may be taken as a concentration of 1 mole per liter rather than at 1 atm. Such a choice is seldom, if ever, used for tables of standard free energies, but it is occasionally found, especially in introductory discussions, for applications to chemical equilibria.

There is one important distinction between the way in which standard states are chosen for enthalpy and for free energy. Both are commonly taken for 1 atm pressure and for the most stable phase under the standard conditions. In selecting a scale for enthalpies, a temperature of 25°C is usually chosen (or sometimes 18°C) and corrections for other temperatures are made by calculations involving the heat capacity.

$$H(T_2) = H(T_1) + \int_{T_1}^{T_2} C_P \, dT$$

The temperature dependence of the free energy, however, is given by equation 23, Chapter 2,

$$\left(\frac{\partial G}{\partial T}\right)_P = -S$$

and, since S can only be known subject to an arbitrary additive constant, the change in free energy with temperature is also subject to an arbitrary additive constant, and is thus unknown.[2] It is therefore necessary to choose the standard state for the specification of free energy to be at the temperature of interest.

CALCULATIONS.   Free-energy changes can now be calculated for specific chemical reactions for particular choices of conditions. Consider first the reaction for the synthesis of ammonia at 25°C when each of the three gases is present at a partial pressure of 5 atm. The standard free-energy change, $\Delta G°$, is -3976 cal/mole (NH_3). Assume the gases are ideal.

$$\tfrac{1}{2} N_2 + \tfrac{3}{2} H_2 \longrightarrow NH_3$$

$$\Delta G = \Delta G° + RT \ln a_{NH_3}/(a_{N_2})^{\frac{1}{2}}(a_{H_2})^{\frac{3}{2}}$$

$$= \Delta G° + RT \ln \frac{P_{NH_3}}{(P_{N_2})^{\frac{1}{2}}(P_{H_2})^{\frac{3}{2}}} = -3976 + 592 \ln \frac{5}{25}$$

$$= -4929 \; cal/mole(NH_3)$$

The standard free-energy change for the decomposition of Ag_2O at 25°C is 2590 cal/mole. The free-energy change for Ag_2O in air (20% O_2) will be slightly different:

$$Ag_2O \longrightarrow 2 \, Ag + \tfrac{1}{2} O_2$$

$$\Delta G = \Delta G° + RT \ln \frac{(a_{Ag})^2(a_{O_2})^{\frac{1}{2}}}{a_{Ag_2O}}$$

Activities of the solids are one and the activity of the oxygen is 0.20 (equal to the pressure in atmospheres).

$$\Delta G = 2{,}590 + 1.987 \times 298 \ln(0.20)^{\frac{1}{2}} = 2{,}590 - 296 \ln 5$$

$$= 2117 \; cal/mole$$

---

[2] The limitation does not apply to finding the change in ΔG (for example, the change in $\Delta G_{reaction}$) with change in temperature. This depends on ΔS, which can be measured. The temperature dependence of fugacity can also be found.

The free-energy change for the dissolution of CaF_2 in water at 25°C containing 0.001 M NaF and 0.0001 M $CaCl_2$ may be calculated as follows. The standard free energies of solid CaF_2 and of CaF_2 as a solute are $-277,700$ and $-264,340$ cal/mole. Thus $\Delta G°$ for the dissolution process is 13,360 cal/mole.

$$CaF_2 \longrightarrow Ca^{++} + 2 F^-$$

$$\Delta G = \Delta G° + RT \ln \frac{(a_{Ca^{++}})(a_{F^-})^2}{a_{CaF_2}}$$

The activity of the solid is 1. Assuming the activity coefficients to be 1, the activities of the ions are equal to the numerical values of the concentrations.

$$\Delta G = 13,360 + 1.987 \times 298 \ln (10^{-4})(10^{-3})^2 = 13,360 + 592 \ln 10^{-10}$$

$$= -250 \text{ cal/mole}$$

We may calculate the free-energy change for the dissolution of HCl gas, at a pressure of 0.10 atm, in water containing 0.50 M HCl. The standard free energies of HCl(g) and HCl(aq) are $-22,769$ and $-31,350$ cal/mole, and (by chosen convention) $a_{HCl(aq)} = a_{H^+} a_{Cl^-}$.

$$\Delta G = \Delta G° + RT \ln \frac{a_{H^+} a_{Cl^-}}{a_{HCl(g)}}$$

$$= -8,581 + 1.987 \times 298 \ln \frac{(0.50)(0.50)}{0.10}$$

$$= -8,045 \text{ cal/mole}$$

Equilibrium Constants

At equilibrium, under constant temperature and pressure, the free-energy change is zero and equation 6 becomes

$$0 = \Delta G° + RT \ln \left(\frac{a_C^c a_D^d}{a_A^a a_B^b}\right)_{eq} = \Delta G° + RT \ln Q(a)_{eq}$$

or

$$\Delta G° = -RT \ln \left(\frac{a_C^c a_D^d}{a_A^a a_B^b}\right)_{eq} \tag{15}$$

The left-hand side, $\Delta G°$, is a constant, obtainable from handbook tables. It depends **only** on (1) the choice of standard states, and (2) the temperature. Therefore, at any given temperature the right-hand side of equation 15 —and therefore $Q(a)_{eq}$—must also be a constant, which is called the *equilibrium constant, K* (or K_{eq}).

$$Q(a)_{eq} = \left(\frac{a_C^c a_D^d}{a_A^a a_B^b}\right)_{eq} = K \tag{16}$$

This equation is really quite a remarkable result, and one that students are often unwilling to accept in its full implications. It says that, despite changes of pressure, concentrations of reactants or products, or the presence of other substances, the particular function of activities represented by $Q(a)$ can assume only **one** value at equilibrium, for a given temperature and choice of standard states by which the activities are defined.[3] The value of $Q(a)$ at equilibrium is determined by equation 15, which can be rewritten as

$$\Delta G° = -RT \ln K \tag{17}$$

All problems involving chemical equilibrium must obey equation 17, since no assumptions are required in its derivation.

There is a strong tendency to misinterpret equation 17. The left-hand side refers to standard state conditions, the right-hand side to equilibrium conditions, but these are **not** the same. It may be helpful to think of the equation in an expanded form:

$$(\Delta G)_{\text{std st}} - (\Delta G)_{\text{equil}} = RT \ln Q_{\text{std st}} - RT \ln Q_{\text{equil}}$$

But now, since $(\Delta G)_{\text{std st}} = \Delta G°$, $(\Delta G)_{\text{equil}} = 0$, $Q_{\text{std st}} = 1$, and $Q_{\text{equil}} = K$, the equation may be written

$$\Delta G° - 0 = 0 - RT \ln K$$

Thus $\Delta G°$ may be considered as a measure of how far the standard-state concentrations (or activities) differ from an equilibrium point, and the equilibrium constant may be considered as a measure of how much the equilibrium concentrations (or activities) differ from their standard-state values (activities equal to 1).

Application of the equilibrium constant is straightforward if each step is taken in turn. Consider, for example, the problem of finding the equilibrium pressures of N_2 and H_2 formed by decomposition of ammonia, initially at 2 atm, at 25°C.

$$NH_3 \longrightarrow \tfrac{1}{2} N_2 + \tfrac{3}{2} H_2$$

$$K = \frac{(a_{N_2})^{\frac{1}{2}}(a_{H_2})^{\frac{3}{2}}}{a_{NH_3}}$$

$$\Delta G° = 3976 \text{ cal/mole} = -RT \ln K$$

$$K = 1.2 \times 10^{-3}$$

In a gaseous system, activities are equal to pressures in atm (assuming

---

[3] Many textbooks state that the equilibrium constant depends upon pressure or upon the presence of other substances, but this is because they are not talking about the equilibrium constant but rather the value of $Q(c)$ at equilibrium, which is not necessarily a constant. The "changes in the equilibrium constant" referred to are really changes in the activity coefficients, or changes in the deviations from ideality. The true equilibrium constant (or "thermodynamic equilibrium constant") is rigorously constant!

ideal gas behavior). The pressures, in turn, are proportional to the numbers of moles so, for a given volume and temperature, it is convenient to think of the chemical reaction in terms of pressures (rather than just moles). Thus, if the initial pressure of NH_3 is 2 atm and x atm decomposes, the chemical equation states that $x/2$ atm of N_2 and $3x/2$ atm of H_2 will be produced, with $2 - x$ atm of NH_3 remaining. The equilibrium condition requires that

$$\frac{(x/2)^{\frac{1}{2}}(3x/2)^{\frac{3}{2}}}{(2 - x)} = 1.2 \times 10^{-3}$$

This is a quadratic equation, with the solution $x = 0.0428$ atm. The equilibrium condition may now be more explicitly interpreted for this example. If 2 atm of ammonia comes to equilibrium with its decomposition products, the equilibrium state will be 1.9572 atm of NH_3, together with 0.0214 atm of N_2 and 0.0642 atm of H_2. Slight further decomposition, at these concentrations, would cause no change in free energy; there is no tendency for further decomposition because the system is now at equilibrium. An equilibrium constant for a reaction involving gases, in which pressures appear as an approximation for activities, is often written K_P.

Consider now the problem of finding the equilibrium pressure of oxygen above Ag_2O at 25°C.

$$Ag_2O \longrightarrow 2\,Ag + \tfrac{1}{2}\,O_2$$

$$K = \frac{(a_{Ag})^2(a_{O_2})^{\frac{1}{2}}}{a_{Ag_2O}}$$

$$\Delta G° = 2590 = -RT \ln K$$

$$K = 0.0125 = (P_{O_2})^{\frac{1}{2}}$$

$$P_{O_2} = 1.56 \times 10^{-4} \text{ atm} = 0.119 \text{ torr}$$

Thus silver oxide, placed in a vacuum system, would decompose until the oxygen pressure reached 0.119 torr. In an atmosphere containing 20% oxygen the reaction will be driven in the other direction, so that silver should react with oxygen to form silver oxide. The slow rate of this reaction is attested by the durability of silver goods. An equilibrium constant for dissociation of a compound is often written K_{diss} or, when the dissociation is into ions, $K_{ionization}$.

For the solubility of CaF_2 in water at 25°C,

$$CaF_2 \longrightarrow Ca^{++} + 2\,F^-$$

$$K = \frac{(a_{Ca^{++}})(a_{F^-})^2}{a_{CaF_2}}$$

$$\Delta G° = 13,360 = -RT \ln K$$

$$K = 1.78 \times 10^{-10}$$

The activity of the solid CaF_2 is 1; assume that activities of the ions are numerically equal to concentrations. From the dissociation equation we find that if the concentration of Ca^{++} is s, the concentration of F^- will be $2s$, so long as there is no other source of these ions than CaF_2. Inserting these symbols into the equation above gives

$$1.78 \times 10^{-10} = s(2s)^2$$

$$s = 3.5 \times 10^{-4} \ M$$

This is the solubility of CaF_2, because each mole of CaF_2 going into solution gives one mole of Ca^{++} ions. Introduction of activity coefficients would probably change the calculated value by something on the order of 20%, which is often negligible in determining solubilities. (Reported experimental values differ by much more than this for some compounds, but such accuracies are entirely adequate for some applications.)

To find the solubility of CaF_2 in 0.5 M NaCl the deviation of activity coefficients from 1 should not be neglected. The equations may be written

$$K = 1.78 \times 10^{-10} = (a_{Ca^{++}})(a_{F^-})^2 = (\gamma_{Ca^{++}})(c_{Ca^{++}})(\gamma_{F^-})^2(c_{F^-})^2$$

$$= Q(\gamma)Q(c)$$

Experimental measurements indicate that $Q(\gamma)$, the correction factor, is on the order of 0.1 for such a solution. Solving for the concentrations as before gives

$$4s^3 = \frac{1.78 \times 10^{-10}}{0.1}$$

$$s = 7.6 \times 10^{-4} \ M$$

The increase in solubility when the other ions (Na^+ and Cl^-) are added is called the *salt effect*. The added salt lowers the activity coefficients of all ions present.

The solubility of CaF_2 in 0.5 M NaF will be smaller because of the *common-ion effect*. This is apparent when we substitute numbers into the equations obtained above.

$$K = 1.78 \times 10^{-10} = Q(\gamma)(c_{Ca^{++}})(c_{F^-})^2$$

Now the concentration of fluoride is no longer equal to twice the concentration of calcium ion, but is $0.5 + 2s$ when the Ca^{++} has the concentration s. The correction term may be assumed the same as for NaCl. Then

$$1.78 \times 10^{-10} = 0.1s(0.5 + 2s)^2$$

Assume first that $2s$ is negligible with respect to 0.5. Then

$$s = \frac{1.78 \times 10^{-10}}{0.1 \times 0.5}$$

$$= 3.5 \times 10^{-9} \ M$$

This answer confirms the assumption that taking s negligible with respect to 0.5 gives a self-consistent, and therefore mathematically valid, solution to the problem. The equilibrium constant for dissolution of a slightly soluble salt in water is called the *solubility product constant,* or K_{sp}.

An orderly procedure in working problems of chemical equilibrium will greatly decrease the opportunity for mistakes. The recommended steps are as follows:

1. Write the chemical reaction, even though it is a familiar one.
2. Write out the equilibrium constant expression, $Q(a)$, in terms of activities and set this equal to K_{eq}.
3. Determine the equilibrium constant for the reaction *as written,* either from the constant given or from standard-state free energies. Note that reversing a reaction inverts the equilibrium constant, and that multiplication of the equation by an integer raises the equilibrium constant to that power.
4. Make the appropriate substitutions of symbols (that is: concentrations, pressures, mole fractions, or unity) for each of the activities. Include activity coefficients if necessary (either numerically or symbolically).
5. Determine, from information given and the stoichiometry of the chemical reaction, what is known about concentrations or pressures.
6. Solve the algebraic equation.
7. Examine the solution to be sure that the answer found is the answer to the question asked and is a reasonable value in terms of the physical problem as stated and the approximations made in the solution of the problem.

Consider, for example, the decomposition of gaseous PH_3 ($\Delta G° = 4,360$ cal/mole at 25°C) to give white phosphorus (solid) and hydrogen gas. If 5 atm of PH_3 in a closed vessel comes to equilibrium with its decomposition products, what will be the final pressure of PH_3? The specific steps of the solution, as described above, are:

1.
$$2\,PH_3 \rightleftharpoons 2\,P + 3\,H_2$$

2.
$$K_{eq} = \frac{a_P^2 a_{H_2}^{\,3}}{a^2_{PH_3}}$$

3.
$$\Delta G° = -8{,}720 = -1.987 \times 298 \ln K$$
$$K = 2.51 \times 10^6$$

4.
$$a_P = 1; \qquad 2.51 \times 10^6 = \frac{P^3_{H_2}}{P^2_{PH_3}}$$

5.
$$2\,PH_3 \longrightarrow 2\,P + 3\,H_2$$
$$5 - 2x \qquad\qquad 3x \qquad\qquad x = \text{pressure, atm}$$
$$2.51 \times 10^6 = (3x)^3/(5 - 2x)^2$$

6. Find the solution to the equation $2.51 \times 10^6(5 - 2x)^2 = 27x^3$.

Because K_{eq} is large, the reaction must be shifted well to the right, so x will be nearly equal to 5/2, and $5 - 2x$ will be very sensitive to x. Therefore, as a first approximation, let $x = 5/2$ on the right-hand side and find

$(5 - 2x)$:

$$(5 - 2x)^2 = 27(5/2)^3/2.51 \times 10^6 = 1.68 \times 10^{-4}$$

$$x = 2.49$$

This calculated value is in excellent agreement with the value assumed, so the calculation is selfconsistent.

    7. The final pressure of PH_3 is $5 - 2x = 0.013$ atm and of H_2, $3x = 7.48$ atm. This is a reasonable answer for the problem given, because $\Delta G°(PH_3) = 4,360$ cal/mole indicates that the PH_3 is quite unstable.

Temperature Dependence of Equilibrium Constants

    The equilibrium constant does vary with temperature. From equation 17, $\ln K = -\Delta G°/RT$, we can find the temperature dependence. Take the derivative with respect to temperature (holding the pressure constant at its standard value), employing equation 30 of Chapter 2.

$$\frac{d \ln K}{dT} = -\frac{d}{dT}(\Delta G°/RT) = \frac{-1}{RT}\frac{d(\Delta G°)}{dT} - \frac{\Delta G°}{R}\frac{d(T^{-1})}{dT}$$

$$= \frac{\Delta S°}{RT} + \frac{\Delta G°}{RT^2} = \frac{T\Delta S° + \Delta G°}{RT^2}$$

and therefore

$$\frac{d \ln K}{dT} = \frac{\Delta H°}{RT^2} \tag{18}$$

The last equation can be integrated, assuming $\Delta H°$ is constant with temperature, to give

$$\ln \frac{K_2}{K_1} = \frac{\Delta H°}{RT_1 T_2}\Delta T \tag{19}$$

In these equations K_2 is the equilibrium constant at the temperature T_2, K_1 the equilibrium constant at T_1, $\Delta H°$ is the enthalpy change for the reaction with all reactants and products in their standard states, and $\Delta T = T_2 - T_1$.

    The similarity of equation 19 to the Clausius-Clapeyron equation (equation 6, Chapter 3) is not accidental. Equations for solubility, for reaction rate constants, and other quantities, have equivalent forms. This form is to be expected because all of these physical properties depend on the system surmounting an energy barrier (represented by the heat of reaction, the heat of vaporization, the heat of solution, or some other such energy, or enthalpy, term) and therefore they depend, in a fundamental way, on the *Boltzmann distribution law,* which is an exponential expression relating numbers of molecules, energy states, and temperature, and which therefore gives rise to a logarithmic temperature dependence.

Electrochemistry

One of the best methods of directly measuring the free-energy change of a chemical reaction is to carry out the reaction in an electrochemical cell. The free-energy change, at constant temperature and pressure, is

$$dG = -\delta w + P\,dV = -\delta w'$$

or

$$\Delta G = -w' \tag{20}$$

where w' is the electrical work. Electrical power, $\mathscr{P}$, is $\mathscr{I}^2\mathscr{R} = \mathscr{E}\mathscr{I}$ and electrical work is power multiplied by time, or potential multiplied by charge:

$$w' = \mathscr{P}t = \mathscr{E}\mathscr{I}t = \mathscr{E}q$$

If the potential $\mathscr{E}$ is in volts, the current $\mathscr{I}$ in amperes, and the time t in seconds, then the resistance $\mathscr{R}$ is in ohms, the charge q is in coulombs, the power $\mathscr{P}$ in watts, and the work w' in joules. A convenient unit of charge is a mole of electrons (6×10^{23} electrons), called a *faraday*. One faraday is 96,487 coulombs. If n moles of electrons (or n "equivalents") are transferred at a potential $\mathscr{E}$ the work done is $w' = \mathscr{E}q = \mathscr{E}(n\mathscr{F})$ and the free-energy change is

$$\Delta G = -n\mathscr{F}\mathscr{E} \tag{21}$$

Substitution of equation 21 into equation 7 gives

$$-n\mathscr{F}\mathscr{E} = -n\mathscr{F}\mathscr{E}^\circ + RT\ln Q(a)$$

and therefore

$$\mathscr{E} = \mathscr{E}^\circ - \frac{RT}{n\mathscr{F}}\ln Q(a) \tag{22}$$

This is now commonly called the Nernst equation. Similarly, by combining equation 21 with equation 17 we obtain

$$\mathscr{E}^\circ = \frac{RT}{n\mathscr{F}}\ln K \tag{23}$$

Writing

$$a_i = \gamma_i c_i$$

for each of the reactants and products, the function Q factors to give

$$Q(a) = Q(\gamma)Q(c)$$

and thus

$$\mathscr{E} = \mathscr{E}^\circ - \frac{RT}{n\mathscr{F}}\ln Q(\gamma) - \frac{RT}{n\mathscr{F}}\ln Q(c)$$

If each of the activity coefficients, γ_i, is unity, then $Q(\gamma) = 1$, $\ln Q(\gamma) = 0$, and

$$(\gamma_i = 1) \qquad\qquad \mathcal{E} = \mathcal{E}° - \frac{RT}{n\mathcal{F}} \ln Q(c) \qquad\qquad (24)$$

The potential depends on the actual activities, or concentrations, of the reactants and products.

Not only ΔG and equilibrium constants can be determined electrochemically, but also ΔH and ΔS. From equation 21 and equation 30 of Chapter 2,

$$\Delta S = -\frac{\partial \Delta G}{\partial T}\Big)_P = n\mathcal{F}\frac{\partial \mathcal{E}}{\partial T}\Big)_P \qquad (25)$$

and therefore, from $\Delta H = \Delta G + T\,\Delta S$, we obtain

$$\Delta H = -n\mathcal{F}\mathcal{E} + n\mathcal{F}T\frac{\partial \mathcal{E}}{\partial T}\Big)_P \qquad (26)$$

HALF-REACTION POTENTIALS. An electrical potential (often called an electrochemical potential) exists for any chemical reaction in which electrons are transferred from one substance to another. Such reactions are called *oxidation-reduction reactions,* or simply *"redox" reactions.* Removal of electrons, as in $Fe \rightarrow Fe^{+3} + 3e$, or $2\,I^- \rightarrow I_2 + 2e$, is called *oxidation;* addition of electrons is called *reduction.*

Electrons enter or leave a device through a metal wire or rod or some other conductor that is called an *electrode.* The *cathode* (from the Greek "down way") is the electrode at which electrons enter any device; the anode (from the Greek "up way") is the electrode at which electrons leave any device. To push electrons through a vacuum tube or electroplating cell, the cathode must be made negative. On the other hand, the electrode at which an electrochemical cell releases electrons is called negative (Figure 1) and this is, by definition, the anode.

The electrochemical potential of a reaction may be considered to be a sum of the potentials of two half reactions, each defined from equation 21 in terms of the

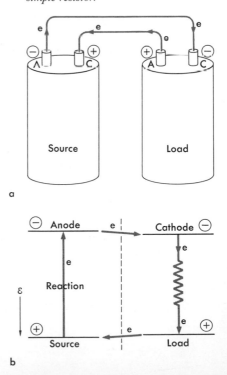

FIGURE 1   *Flow of electrons in an electrical circuit. (a) A voltmeter placed across the terminals of a cell producing current will show the anode (source of electrons) to be negative with respect to the cathode. The cathode (point of entry of electrons) is negative for a device without an internal source of current. (b) A plot of electrical potential for the circuit shows that the chemical reaction pumps electrons to a large negative potential. They return to their starting point by passing through the "load," represented here as a simple resistor.*

CHEMICAL   EQUILIBRIUM

free-energy changes. Let ΔG_A be the free-energy change for the anode reaction (electrons leaving, hence oxidation), ΔG_C be the free-energy change for
the cathode reaction (electrons entering, hence reduction), and ΔG be the
free-energy change for the total reaction. Free energy changes are additive, so

$$\Delta G = -n\mathcal{F}\mathcal{E} = \Delta G_A + \Delta G_C = -n_A\mathcal{F}\mathcal{E}_A - n_C\mathcal{F}\mathcal{E}_C$$

and because $n_A = n_C = n$ for any balanced reaction,

$$\mathcal{E} = \mathcal{E}_A + \mathcal{E}_C \tag{27}$$

Note that the potentials are independent of n and thus independent of the
amount of reaction. That is, the potential of a half-reaction such as

$$\tfrac{1}{2}M^{++} + e \longrightarrow \tfrac{1}{2}M$$

is identically the same as the potential of the half-reaction

$$M^{++} + 2e \longrightarrow M$$

In nearly all electrochemical cells there is a small additional term that
should be included on the right-hand side of equation 27, arising from the
contact between dissimilar solutions. Like $\mathcal{E}_A$ and $\mathcal{E}_C$, these "junction
potentials" cannot be measured, nor can they be calculated by thermodynamics. They can, however, be estimated, using theories involving diffusion
rates, and are usually sufficiently small in practice that they can be ignored
for present purposes.

It is not possible to measure $\mathcal{E}_A$ or $\mathcal{E}_C$ separately, because measurements
can be made only when the circuit has been completed. However, it is
possible to measure total cell potentials. Then, by choosing an arbitrary
value for some half-reaction potential as a reference level, other half-
reaction potentials can be determined relative to this arbitrary reference.
The half-reaction chosen for this purpose is

$$2e + 2\,H^+ \longrightarrow H_2$$

for which $\mathcal{E}^\circ$ (the potential with all reactants and products at unit activity)
is assigned the value zero. Then, for example, since the standard potential
of the cell reaction

$$Zn + 2\,H^+ \longrightarrow H_2 + Zn^{++}$$

has been found to be 0.763 volt, it follows that the standard potential for
the half reaction

$$Zn \longrightarrow Zn^{++} + 2e$$

must be 0.763 volt. Then, since $\mathcal{E}^\circ$ for the reaction

$$Zn + Cu^{++} \longrightarrow Cu + Zn^{++}$$

Table 1 STANDARD ELECTRODE POTENTIALS, 25°C
(STANDARD REDUCTION POTENTIALS)

Reaction	$\mathscr{E}°$ (volt)	Reaction	$\mathscr{E}°$ (volt)
$Li^+ + e \longrightarrow Li$	-3.045	$Cu^{++} + e \longrightarrow Cu^+$	0.153
$K^+ + e \longrightarrow K$	-2.925	$SO_4^= + 4\,H^+ + 2e \longrightarrow$	
$Na^+ + e \longrightarrow Na$	-2.71	$\quad H_2SO_3 + H_2O$	0.20
$Mg^{++} + 2e \longrightarrow Mg$	-2.37	$AgCl + e \longrightarrow Ag + Cl^-$	0.222
$Al^{+++} + 3e \longrightarrow Al$	-1.67	$Cu^{++} + 2e \longrightarrow Cu$	0.337
$Mn(OH)_2 + 2e \longrightarrow$		$Cu^+ + e \longrightarrow Cu$	0.522
$\quad Mn + 2\,OH^-$	-1.47	$I_2 + 2e \longrightarrow 2\,I^-$	0.534
$Zn^{++} + 2e \longrightarrow Zn$	-0.763	$MnO_4^- + e \longrightarrow MnO_4^=$	0.54
$Cr^{++} + 2e \longrightarrow Cr$	-0.74	$MnO_4^- + 2\,H_2O + 3e$	
$2\,CO_2(g) + 2\,H^+ + 2e$		$\quad \longrightarrow MnO_2 + 4\,OH^-$	0.57
$\quad \longrightarrow H_2C_2O_4(aq)$	-0.49	$O_2 + 2\,H^+ + 2e \longrightarrow H_2O_2$	0.682
$Fe^{++} + 2e \longrightarrow Fe$	-0.440	$Fe^{+++} + e \longrightarrow Fe^{++}$	0.771
$Cr^{+++} + e \longrightarrow Cr^{++}$	-0.41	$Hg_2^{++} + 2e \longrightarrow 2\,Hg$	0.789
$Cd^{++} + 2e \longrightarrow Cd$	-0.402	$Ag^+ + e \longrightarrow Ag$	0.7991
$AgI + e \longrightarrow Ag + I^-$	-0.151	$Hg^{++} + 2e \longrightarrow Hg$	0.854
$Sn^{++} + 2e \longrightarrow Sn$	-0.136	$2\,Hg^{++} + 2e \longrightarrow Hg_2^{++}$	0.919
$Pb^{++} + 2e \longrightarrow Pb$	-0.126	$NO_3^- + 4\,H^+ + 3e \longrightarrow NO + 2\,H_2O$	0.96
$O_2 + H_2O + 2e \longrightarrow$		$Cr_2O_7^= + 14\,H^+ + 6e \longrightarrow$	
$\quad HO_2^- + OH^-$	-0.076	$\quad 2\,Cr^{+++} + 7\,H_2O$	1.33
$Cu(NH_3)_4^{++} + 2e \longrightarrow$		$Cl_2 + 2e \longrightarrow 2\,Cl^-$	1.359
$\quad Cu + 4\,NH_3$	-0.05	$MnO_4^- + 8\,H^+ + 5e \longrightarrow$	
$Fe^{+++} + 3e \longrightarrow Fe$	-0.036	$\quad Mn^{++} + 4\,H_2O$	1.52
$2\,H^+ + 2e \longrightarrow H_2$	0.0000	$Ce^{++++} + e \longrightarrow Ce^{+++}$	1.61
$AgBr + e \longrightarrow Ag + Br^-$	0.073	$MnO_4^- + 4\,H^+ + 3e \longrightarrow$	
$Hg_2Br_2 + 2e \longrightarrow 2\,Hg + 2\,Br^-$	0.14	$\quad MnO_2 + 2\,H_2O$	1.67
$Sn^{++++} + 2e \longrightarrow Sn^{++}$	0.15	$H_2O_2 + 2\,H^+ + 2e \longrightarrow 2\,H_2O$	1.77

has been measured to be 1.100 volt, it follows that for

$$2e + Cu^{++} \longrightarrow Cu$$

the standard potential is $\mathscr{E}° = 0.337$ volt. We can proceed in this fashion to find the potential for any half reaction on this arbitrary scale. Reversal of a cell reaction changes the sign of a potential.[4] The more positive a half-reaction potential, the greater the tendency of that half reaction to proceed as written. (But it should be kept in mind that the reaction may be too slow to observe or that some other spontaneous reaction may occur instead.) Some standard potentials for reduction half-reactions are given in Table 1. According to the Stockholm Convention, such standard reduction potentials are called *standard electrode potentials*. If the reaction is written in reverse order, $\mathscr{E}°$ will have the opposite sign and is called the *standard*

---

[4] An electrical potential difference is the work required to move a unit charge between two points, just as a gravitational potential difference is the work required to move a unit mass between two points. The gravitational potential difference for a well is positive if the top is measured with respect to the bottom, or negative if the bottom is measured with respect to the top, and an electrical potential that is positive if the cathode is measured with respect to the anode will be negative if the reaction is reversed. (The "standard electrode potential" includes a choice of sign in the definition, but "standard potential" simply means that the reactants and products are in their standard states.)

oxidation potential. Tabulations of half-reaction potentials are often given for oxidation half-reactions.[5]

CALCULATIONS OF CELL POTENTIALS.   A few examples will illustrate the applications of standard potentials of half reactions. Consider the cell reaction

$$2\ Fe^{+++} + Cu \longrightarrow Cu^{++} + 2\ Fe^{++}$$

This consists of the two half reactions,

$$2e + 2\ Fe^{+++} \longrightarrow 2\ Fe^{++}$$

$$Cu \longrightarrow Cu^{++} + 2e$$

The standard potential for the first is taken directly from Table 1, that for the second is obtained from the table simply by changing the sign (because the reaction is the reverse of that given in the table). Thus

$$\mathcal{E}° = 0.771 + (-0.337) = 0.434\ volt$$

The positive cell potential indicates that the original reaction will proceed as written, with substances at unit activity.

The potential for the cell shown in Figure 2, at 25°C, may be found as follows. From Table 1,

$$\mathcal{E}° = 0.763 + 0.337 = 1.100\ volt$$

FIGURE 2   *A simple electrochemical cell. An electrode of zinc (the anode) and an electrode of copper (the cathode) dip into solutions containing Zn^{++} and Cu^{++} ions of known concentrations. A voltmeter or potentiometer measures the potential difference and provides the opposing force that establishes equilibrium (allowing ideally only an infinitesimal extent of reaction).*

$$\mathcal{E} = \mathcal{E}° - \frac{RT}{n\mathcal{F}} \ln \frac{a_{Cu} a_{Zn^{++}}}{a_{Zn} a_{Cu^{++}}}$$

$$= 1.100\ volt$$

$$- \frac{(8.314\ joule/mole\text{-}deg)\,(298\ deg)}{(2\ equiv/mole)\,(96{,}487\ coul/equiv)} \ln \frac{0.01}{0.1}$$

$$= 1.130\ volt$$

assuming the solid metals, Zn and Cu, are at unit activity (pure and not seriously strained). The activities of the ions have been approximated by their concentrations.

The concentration correction factor, $(RT/n\mathcal{F})\ \ln\ Q(a)$, appears sufficiently often that it is helpful to carry out a partial evaluation. At room temperature, 25°C, we may write

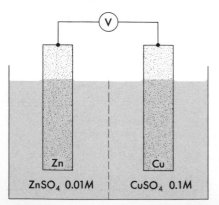

Zn

Cu

ZnSO₄ 0.01M

CuSO₄ 0.1M

[5] For more half-reaction potentials see especially W. Latimer, *Oxidation Potentials,* 2nd ed., Prentice-Hall, Englewood Cliffs, N.J., 1952.

$$\frac{RT}{n\mathscr{F}} \ln Q(a) = \frac{8.314 \times 298.15}{n \times 96{,}487} \text{volt} \times 2.3026 \log Q(a)$$

(25°C) $$\frac{RT}{n\mathscr{F}} \ln Q(a) = \frac{0.05915}{n} \log Q(a)$$ (28)

Equation 22 may therefore be written

(25°C) $$\mathscr{E} = \mathscr{E}° - \frac{0.05915}{n} \log Q(a)$$ (22a)

The Nernst equation may also be applied to half-reaction potentials. For example, the potential of the reduction half-reaction

$$Zn^{++} + 2e \longrightarrow Zn$$

would be

$$\mathscr{E} = \mathscr{E}° - \frac{RT}{n\mathscr{F}} \ln \frac{a_{Zn}}{a_{Zn^{++}}}$$

or, at 25°C,

$$\mathscr{E} = -.763 - \frac{0.05915}{2} \log \frac{a_{Zn}}{a_{Zn^{++}}}$$

(The electrons should, in principle, also appear in this expression, but the "activity" of the electrons is unknown, and when this reduction half-reaction is combined with an oxidation half-reaction, the electron terms will drop out.) Similarly, for the oxidation half-reaction

$$Zn \longrightarrow Zn^{++} + 2e$$

the potential, at 25°C, would be

$$\mathscr{E} = 0.763 - \frac{0.05915}{2} \log \frac{a_{Zn^{++}}}{a_{Zn}}$$

Although space does not permit an adequate discussion of the problem of reversibility, it should be pointed out that not all chemical reactions can be carried out in electrochemical cells, and even many that can will not be reversed by a change of potential. The first requirement for a well-behaved electrochemical cell must be that the reaction will proceed as desired and be capable of reversal. To achieve quantitative agreement with the equations of thermodynamics, however, the requirements are more stringent. The chemical reaction must be thermodynamically reversible, so that an infinitesimal change of potential is sufficient to reverse the flow of current and the direction of chemical reaction. Discussions of the problems encountered in irreversible electrochemical systems may be found in more advanced works under the listings of "overvoltage," "polarization," and "junction potentials."

CELL NOTATION.   A very convenient shorthand notation has been developed for writing electrochemical cells. The cell shown in Figure 2 can be represented by

$$Zn/ZnSO_4(0.01\ M)//CuSO_4(0.1\ M)/Cu$$

A cell in which the reaction is the displacement of hydrogen by zinc can be written

$$Zn/Zn^{++}//H^+/H_2,\ Pt$$

the platinum serving as the electrical contact to the solution, with hydrogen gas bubbled around the platinum. Although there are minor differences among authors concerning separating components with commas and shilling marks, generally one of these marks will separate substances in direct contact. The // indicates a junction between two different solutions, which are commonly connected by a "salt bridge," such as a U tube containing concentrated KCl solution and dipping into the two solutions.

The direction of the cell reaction is determined by the convention that the electrode on the left is the anode.[6]

APPLICATIONS OF ELECTRODE POTENTIALS.   Electrochemistry has important applications in physical chemistry, analytical chemistry, descriptive inorganic chemistry, preparative inorganic and organic chemistry, biochemistry, and metallurgy. Electrochemical measurements provide an accurate means of obtaining the thermodynamic properties of a reaction, including ΔH, ΔS, and ΔG. These thermodynamic properties depend, in turn, on the exact nature of the reaction, including the charges on the ions participating. Because the potentials depend on concentrations, information is available on the concentrations of individual ions in solution for analytical purposes or for determining solubilities.

Electrode potentials are often more convenient than free energies for prediction of which reactions will be spontaneous. For example, oxidizing agents can be put in order of oxidizing powers by reference to the standard potentials for the corresponding reactions. Often an oxidizing agent can be found that is just strong enough to do the job desired and not so strong that it will oxidize other substances present in the mixture. Electrode potentials are the basis of studies of corrosion and electro-refining of metals.

Problems

1. The standard free energies of NO_2 and N_2O_4 at $25°C$ are 12,250 and 23,360 cal/mole. Find the equilibrium constant for the reaction

$$2\ NO_2 \longrightarrow N_2O_4$$

---

[6] There are very few conventions that need to be memorized, although these few can be expressed in a bewildering variety of forms. One convention is that the anode (where electrons leave the cell) is on the left in these condensed cell descriptions. A mnemonic for remembering this is a partial acrostic based on the word "always": A̲node ... L̲eft ... W̲ ... A̲ ... Y̲ ... S̲. Another convention is that the term *standard electrode potential* means the same as *standard reduction potential*. A third is that a positive potential for a cell corresponds to a spontaneous reaction, as implied by equation 21.

2. For each of the following reactions, set up the equilibrium constant expression, in terms of activities, and make the appropriate substitutions of symbols (concentrations, pressures, mole fractions, or unity) for the activities:

$\qquad$ a. $Cu^{++} + H_2S(aq) \longrightarrow CuS + 2\ H^+$

$\qquad$ b. $2\ HgO \longrightarrow 2\ Hg + O_2$

$\qquad$ c. $NaHCO_3 + HCl \xrightarrow[H_2O]{} CO_2(g) + H_2O + NaCl$

$\qquad$ d. $AcOEt \qquad + H_2O \xrightarrow[H_2O]{H^+} AcOH \quad + \quad EtOH$
$\qquad$ (ethyl acetate) $\qquad\qquad$ (acetic acid) $\quad$ (ethanol)

3. The standard free energies of benzene and cyclohexane are 30,989 and 6,800 cal/mole at 25°C. Find the equilibrium constant for the reduction of benzene with hydrogen at 25°C:

$$C_6H_6\ (liq) + 3\ H_2 \longrightarrow C_6H_{12}\ (liq)$$

If equilibrium is reached with 5 atm H_2 gas present, what is the mole fraction of benzene left in the cyclohexane liquid produced?

4. What effect will the addition of an inert gas have on the equilibrium point of the gas-phase reaction

$$N_2O_4 \longrightarrow 2\ NO_2$$

if the *volume* is maintained constant?

5. What effect will the addition of an inert gas have on the equilibrium point of the gas-phase reaction

$$N_2O_4 \longrightarrow 2\ NO_2$$

if the *total pressure* is maintained constant?

6. For the reaction

$$CO + 2\ H_2 \longrightarrow CH_3OH$$

$\Delta G° = -3220$ cal at 700°K. Find the percentage decomposition of methanol, at this temperature and constant volume, if the initial pressure of pure methanol is 5 atm.

7. Water and solid sulfur can react to form SO_2 and H_2S according to the equation

$$H_2O\ (gas) + \tfrac{3}{2}\ S \longrightarrow \tfrac{1}{2}\ SO_2 + H_2S$$

The standard free energies are, for H_2O (gas), $-54,636$, for H_2S (gas), $-7,890$, and for SO_2 (gas), $-71,740$ cal/mole, at 25°C.

$\qquad$ a. Find the equilibrium constant for the reaction as written.

$\qquad$ b. Calculate the pressures of SO_2 and H_2S to be expected in equilibrium with solid sulfur and moist air (vapor pressure of water $= 23.8$ torr) at 25°C, assuming gases to be ideal.

8. The reaction

$$2\ SO_2 + O_2 \longrightarrow 2\ SO_3$$

is of considerable industrial importance. Starting with one-fourth atm of SO_3 vapor at 25°C, in a fixed volume, find the equilibrium pressure of SO_3 and hence the percentage dissociation.

9. The standard free energy of HI at 250°C is -2570 cal/mole.

  a. Find $\Delta G°$ and the equilibrium constant for the reaction, at 250°C,

$$\tfrac{1}{2} H_2 + \tfrac{1}{2} I_2 \longrightarrow HI$$

  b. Find $\Delta G°$ and the equilibrium constant for the reaction, at 250°C,

$$H_2 + I_2 \longrightarrow 2 HI$$

  How does this K compare with the K from part a?

  c. Find ΔG for the reaction, at 250°C,

$$H_2 \text{ (1 atm)} + I_2 \text{ (1 atm)} \longrightarrow 2 HI \text{ (0 atm)}$$

  d. If 1 atm of HI at 250°C is placed in a vessel and allowed to reach equilibrium with its decomposition products at this temperature, what will be the final pressure of HI?

10. The solubility product constant, K_{sp}, for MgF_2 at room temperature is 7.1×10^{-9}. Assuming activity coefficients are unity, find the solubility of MgF_2

  a. in water

  b. in 0.01 M NaF solution

  Addition of ions to a dilute solution will decrease the values of activity coefficients. Would the addition of Na_2SO_4 increase or decrease the solubility of MgF_2?

11. Find $\Delta G°$ for the process of dissolving MgF_2 in water. Is this positive or negative? Explain why, in terms of what will happen when MgF_2 is added to water.

12. The solubility products for barium oxalate at 18°C are given below.

  (A) $BaC_2O_4 \cdot 2 H_2O$ $K_{sp} = 1.2 \times 10^{-7}$
  (B) $BaC_2O_4 \cdot \tfrac{1}{2} H_2O$ $K_{sp} = 2.2 \times 10^{-7}$

  a. Assuming only (A) is present in the solid phase, find the concentration of Ba^{++} ion in aqueous solution in equilibrium with this solid.

  b. Assuming only (B) is present in the solid phase, find the concentration of Ba^{++} ion in aqueous solution in equilibrium with this solid.

  c. Describe what will happen if 1 gm of (A) and 1 gm of (B) are added to 100 ml of water at 18°C under 1 atm pressure.

  d. How many phases will be present at equilibrium? What are they?

13. The dissociation constant of H_2S in water solution is 9.1×10^{-8}:

$$H_2S \longrightarrow H^+ + HS^-$$

  (The second dissociation, to give $S^=$, can be ignored here.) Find the concentration of hydrogen ion in 0.1 M H_2S solution.

14. The dissociation constant of benzoic acid is 6.30×10^{-5} at 25°C. Find the concentration of hydrogen ion

  a. in 0.001 M benzoic acid solution

  b. in solution containing 0.001 M benzoic acid plus 0.01 M sodium benzoate (Benzoic acid dissociates to give one hydrogen ion, BH $\longrightarrow$ $B^- + H^+$, and sodium benzoate dissociates completely to give $B^- + Na^+$.)

15. For the cell

$$Zn/Zn^{++}(a = 0.01)//Ag^+(a = 0.5)/Ag$$

a. Write the over-all cell reaction.
b. What is $\mathcal{E}°$?
c. What is $\mathcal{E}$?
d. Is the reaction spontaneous?

16. Find the equilibrium constant for the reaction, at 25°C,

$$2 \ Fe^{++} + Hg_2^{++} \longrightarrow 2 \ Hg + 2 \ Fe^{+++}$$

17. The potential of the cell

$$H_2(1 \ atm)/HCl(0.01 \ M), \ AgCl(s)/Ag(s)$$

is 0.464 volt at 25°C.
a. Will the potential be increased or decreased by adding NaCl to a concentration of 0.10 M?
b. Will the potential be increased or decreased by alloying the silver with gold?
c. Is the silver the anode or cathode?
d. As the cell is written, will electrons in the external circuit flow from left to right or from right to left?

18. The Weston normal cell is Cd-Hg/CdSO$_4$/Hg$_2$SO$_4$/Hg, for which the potential is $\mathcal{E} = 1.0183[1 - 4.06 \times 10^{-5}(t - 20) - 9.5 \times 10^{-7}(t - 20)^2 + 1 \times 10^{-8}(t - 20)^3]$ volt at $t°$C. Find ΔH for this cell at 20°C.

19. The cadmium-calomel cell

$$Cd + Hg_2Cl_2 \longrightarrow Cd^{++} + 2 \ Cl^- + 2 \ Hg$$

has been found to have a potential that varies with temperature according to the equation

$$\mathcal{E}° = 0.6708 - 1.02 \times 10^{-4}(T - 298) - 2.4 \times 10^{-6}(T - 298)^2$$

with T in °K and $\mathcal{E}°$ in volts. For the cell reaction at 40°C, calculate
a. $\Delta G°$ b. $\Delta H°$ c. $\Delta S°$

20. For the cell

$$Pt, \ H_2(1 \ atm)/HCl/AgCl/Ag$$

in which the electrolyte also contained 0.001 M NaCl, the measured potential, at 25°C, was found to be 0.724 volt. What is the pH of the solution, assuming activities equal to concentrations?

21. Write the reaction to be expected if a block of Mg is attached to a steel ship hull. Will the ship be oxidized or protected from oxidation?

22. Find an oxidizing agent capable of oxidizing Hg to Hg$_2^{++}$ without appreciable formation of Hg^{++}.

23. Predict the products of the following reactions:
a. HNO$_3$ + Hg $\longrightarrow$
b. HNO$_3$ + Hg$_2^{++}$ $\longrightarrow$
c. Hg + Hg^{++} $\longrightarrow$

5

Heat Engines

and Absolute Zero

Many innovations of thought and technology contributed to the Industrial Revolution, but certainly a major factor in its development was the replacement of human and animal power by the power of the steam engine and, later, by power from the internal combustion engine. Thermodynamics, too, owes much of its early development to these engines that convert heat to work. It was through his studies of "heat engines" in the early 19th century that the young Frenchman, Sadi Carnot, discovered the importance of entropy, and even today the heat engine is considered important as a means of demonstrating the principles of classical thermodynamics. But the principles of the heat engine are also of great practical importance in modern technology and in current research. New devices are constantly being sought to convert thermal energy into electrical power. One way of stating the second law is that work can be totally converted to heat but heat cannot be totally converted to work in a cyclic, isothermal process. Thermodynamics provides an understanding of the possible effectiveness, and the inherent limitations, of all devices to convert thermal energy into work. The theory of heat engines is also important to a discussion of absolute zero and the third law of thermodynamics.

Heat Engines and Heat Pumps

The essential ingredients of a steam engine are a boiler and a source of heat for it; a cylinder—into which the steam from the boiler can expand —fitted with a piston against which the gas will push, performing work (and therefore losing energy and becoming cooled); and means for further cooling and venting the expanded steam so that the piston can be returned to its initial position. In the operation of the engine, heat is put into the engine at some elevated temperature, the engine itself does work on its surroundings (transmitted by the shaft of the piston), and a portion of the thermal energy taken in is discharged, as heat, at a lower temperature (into the cooling water). The energy transfers are represented in Figure 1.

The "efficiency" of a heat engine is defined to be the output, w, divided by the input, q_u, which is the heat put into the engine at the upper temperature, T_u:

$$\text{efficiency} = \frac{w}{q_u} \tag{1}$$

For a complete cycle, $q_u + q_l - w = \Delta E = 0$, and q_u is positive, q_l, the heat absorbed by the heat engine at the lower temperature, is negative, and w, the work done by the heat engine, is positive. Therefore $q_u > w$ and the efficiency is necessarily less than 1.

It is possible to operate such a device in reverse. If a gas at a low temperature is compressed by a piston driven from an external source, the gas will be heated and can give up heat to the surroundings at an elevated temperature. A heat engine operated in this fashion is often called a *heat pump*, since the net effect is to absorb heat at a lower temperature and discharge it at a higher temperature, the device being externally powered by the application of work.

CARNOT'S THEOREM.   The possibility of reversing a heat engine leads to an instructive "thought experiment." Assume two heat engines, A and B, are available which can be operated between the same two temperatures and of which at least one (B) is thermodynamically reversible. Assume, also, that the efficiency, w/q_u, is greater for engine A than for engine B. The two engines can then be coupled together as shown in Figure 2. Engine A drives engine B in reverse, supplying work and some heat at the

FIGURE 1   *Schematic representation of a heat engine.*

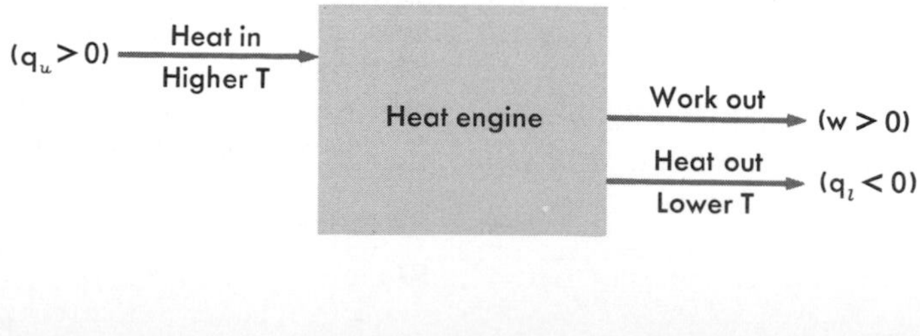

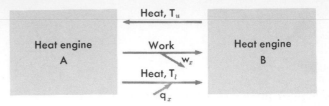

FIGURE 2 *Schematic representation of two reversible heat engines coupled together. It is assumed that the efficiencies are different, so extra work (w_x) is drawn off and extra heat (q_x) is supplied at the lower temperature. The assumption is untenable.*

lower temperature; engine B requires only part of the work output of engine A in order to supply all the heat, at the upper temperature, required to operate engine A, because $(w/q_u)_A > (w/q_u)_B$. The extra work can be diverted to other applications, the energy required coming from the low-temperature heat source. Such a combination is clearly a perpetual-motion machine (of the second kind), which we know is impossible, both from experience and from the second law of thermodynamics. The conclusion is that the efficiency of engine A cannot be greater than the efficiency of the reversible engine B, as had been assumed. Nor can the efficiency of engine B exceed that of engine A if A is reversible, for then the labeling is arbitrary and they could be operated in the reverse direction.

This conclusion is known as *Carnot's theorem: The efficiencies of any two reversible heat engines, operating between the same two temperatures, are the same and this is the maximum efficiency for any heat engine operating between these two temperatures.*

From Carnot's theorem we can see that the nature of the "working fluid"—whether steam, ideal gas, mercury, or any other vapor, liquid, or vapor-liquid combination—cannot change the efficiency, nor can the nature of the cyclic process alter the efficiency, so long as the steps are reversible. The efficiency will, in practice, be decreased by friction and non-reversible heat transfers, but these are differences associated with the departure from reversibility.

It is sufficient, therefore, to choose a very simple cyclic process, employing an ideal gas. The results will be applicable to any real device, apart from corrections for irreversibility.

CARNOT'S CYCLE. The cycle most conveniently treated is called the "Carnot cycle"; it consists of an isothermal reversible expansion at the upper temperature, an adiabatic reversible expansion from the upper temperature to the lower temperature, an isothermal reversible compression at the lower temperature, and an adiabatic reversible compression from the lower to the upper temperature. More briefly, it alternates isothermal and adiabatic steps.

The important equations of the Carnot cycle may be obtained quite easily. For the reversible, isothermal step at T_1, $\Delta E_1 = 0$ and therefore

$$w_1 = q_1 = T_1 \Delta S_1$$

For the reversible adiabatic step ($T_1 \rightarrow T_2$), q is zero and therefore ΔS is zero. In the reversible isothermal step at T_2, $\Delta E_2 = 0$ and

$$w_2 = q_2 = T_2 \Delta S_2$$

and in the reversible adiabatic step returning from T_2 to T_1, q is zero and ΔS is zero.

Now we note that for the over-all process,

$$\Delta S = \Delta S_1 + \Delta S_2 = 0$$

because the engine has undergone a complete cycle. It follows that

$$\Delta S_1 = -\Delta S_2$$

Also, because $\Delta E = 0$ for the complete cycle,

$$w = q = q_1 + q_2 = (T_1 - T_2)\,\Delta S_1$$

Let ΔS_1 be represented by the symbol κ (Greek kappa). The important equations are then

$$q_1 = \kappa T_1 \tag{2}$$

$$q_2 = -\kappa T_2 \tag{3}$$

$$w = \kappa(T_1 - T_2) = \kappa\,\Delta T \tag{4}$$

with q_1 the heat absorbed by the engine at T_1, q_2 the heat absorbed by the engine at T_2, and w the total work done by the engine in a complete cycle. These three equations must apply to any reversible heat engine. Only the value of κ will vary from one engine to another, for a given choice of T_1 and T_2.

APPLICATIONS OF HEAT ENGINES AND HEAT PUMPS.   A heat engine producing net work ($\kappa > 0$) has a maximum efficiency equal to that of a reversible engine. From equations 2 and 4 this is

$$\text{efficiency} = \frac{w}{q_1} = \frac{\Delta T}{T_1} \tag{5}$$

For example, a steam engine operating between 100°C and 20°C has a maximum possible efficiency of

$$\text{eff} = \frac{w}{q_1} = \frac{\Delta T}{T_1} = \frac{80}{373} = 21.4\%$$

Steam engines can be designed to operate with superheated steam, with a resultant improvement in possible performance. Operating between 200°C and 20°C, the maximum possible efficiency would be

$$\text{eff} = \frac{180}{473} = 38.0\%$$

This is nearly twice as high, although it still leaves ample room for improvement by moving to higher-temperature materials. The possible gains in efficiency must, of course, be balanced by increased costs of construction of high-temperature engines.

Equation 5 applies to any "steam engine," whether it uses steam, mercury, or some other fluid. It applies also to internal combustion engines, turbine engines, jet engines, and thermoelectric (Peltier) devices. Many other considerations enter into the total performance characteristics of each of these heat engines, but it is of inestimable help to be able to calculate the efficiency in the limit of the equilibrium or reversible operation of any device, no matter how novel or complicated the device may be.

The limitation on the possible efficiency of converting heat to work is intimately associated with the second law. From the second law (equation 6, Chapter 2) one can derive Carnot's theorem, or from Carnot's theorem one can derive the second law. Work can be converted completely to heat in an isothermal process, but it is not possible to totally convert heat into work in an isothermal process without other changes occurring.

Operation of a heat engine in reverse, as a heat pump, will remove heat from the low-temperature heat reservoir and add heat to the high-temperature reservoir. This is the principle of a refrigerator; the low-temperature region is cooled by this removal of heat.

Assume a room is to be kept at $25°C$ when the surroundings are at $0°C$. If 1 kilowatt hour (3.6 megajoule) of electrical energy is passed through an electrical heater, consisting of a resistance coil, 3.6 megajoule of heat will be added to the room. We may ask how much heat can be added to the room if this same electrical energy drives a heat pump. The answer is given by equation 5.

$$\frac{w}{q_1} = \frac{25}{298}$$

$$q_1 = \frac{298}{25} w = 11.92 \, w = 42.9 \text{ megajoule}$$

Thus it is not only possible to "pump heat" with a heat engine, but it is actually far more effective (about 12 times more effective in this example) than the direct conversion of the work to heat. The effectiveness of this method will increase as ΔT becomes smaller; it is easier to pump energy up a small hill than up a large one.

Often we are more interested in the amount of heat removed from the low-temperature reservoir. For example, if a room is at $25°C$ and the inside of a refrigerator is to be maintained at $0°C$, we would like to find the relationship between w and q_2. From equations 3 and 4,

$$\frac{w}{-q_2} = \frac{\Delta T}{T_2} \tag{6}$$

Inserting the appropriate temperatures we find that

$$-q_2 = \frac{T_2}{\Delta T} w = \frac{273}{25} w = 10.92 \, w$$

Thus, for example, the 1 kwh of electrical energy considered previously could remove 39.3 megajoule of heat from a refrigerator if the refrigerator were an ideal heat pump.

It should be noted that the difference in magnitude of the heat pumped into the high-temperature reservoir (11.92 w) and that pumped out of the low-temperature reservoir (10.92 w) is exactly equal to w, as is required for conservation of energy.

The principle of the heat pump has been understood for a long time and has been widely applied in refrigeration. Its application to heating problems has been much slower, largely because of engineering problems and associated economic considerations. Whereas there is no simple alternative to the heat pump for use in refrigeration (except perhaps frequent ice deliveries), heating can of course be accomplished without the aid of a heat pump, simply by burning fuel. This same fuel could, however, be burned to operate a heat engine that would produce work, which might then be transmitted by a direct mechanical linkage or by turning a generator that would send electrical power along transmission lines to an electrical motor. If this work were then to drive a heat pump, more heat could be put into a room than if the original fuel had been burned to heat the room more directly.

Unfortunately, the inefficiency of the heat engine in the first stage tends to offset the effectiveness of the heat pump in the second. Because of the necessary inefficiency in its production, a watt-hour of electricity is generally more expensive than a supply of fuel of comparable energy value,[1] although the electricity is potentially more valuable. However, large heat-engine installations can have over-all efficiencies as high as 35–40%, and thus electric power is not exorbitantly costly; in fact, the increased effectiveness of heat pumps leaves room for many losses along the way to what can prove to be a substantial net gain. The engineering problems are being solved and heat pumps are becoming far more common, especially in regions where the winter heating load and the summer air-conditioning load are comparable and can be met by a single "reversible" installation.

The Third Law of Thermodynamics

As we have seen, the first law of thermodynamics deals with the conservation of energy as it is transformed and transferred between the system and surroundings. Although temperature is important in measuring energy changes, it enters only as temperature differences, for which the scale is quite arbitrary. The second law of thermodynamics predicts which of the many conceivable transformations and transferrals of energy can actually occur, given sufficient time. In the definition of the entropy function an "absolute" temperature appears, which recurs in the equations for phase equilibrium, in the expressions for the efficiencies of heat engines, and in other applications of the second law. The third law of thermodynamics is comparatively recent, having been first proposed early in the present cen-

---

[1] Hydroelectric power (or electric power from nuclear reactors), because of the large initial investment, often costs at least as much to produce as electric power from steam turbines employing conventional fuels. (Excess costs are charged to flood control, irrigation, or navigation.) Also, it should not be forgotten that the major cost of electricity (or of fuel) in the home is in distribution. Even if electric power were free at the generating station there would be only a minor change in price to the small consumer.

tury. There are several forms suggested for this additional postulate, but all are intimately involved with the "absolute" temperature scale, and particularly with the absolute zero of temperature.

DETERMINATION OF THE ABSOLUTE TEMPERATURE SCALE. It has not been possible to achieve the absolute zero of temperature and there is good reason to believe that it cannot be reached, although temperatures of 0.001°K and below have been accessible for many years. The importance of the zero lies not so much in the field of low-temperature experimentation, as important as this may be, as in the much larger field of experimentation at moderate and high temperatures. The absolute temperature scale is important at room temperature because there are experimentally measurable quantities that have values predictable by theory from the absolute temperature. Thus we can, in turn, use these room-temperature measurements to determine the absolute temperature and hence to determine the zero point.

As a specific example, we may consider an experiment in which a heat engine operates between two temperatures, one of which is the boiling point of water and the other the freezing point of water. The amount of heat absorbed from the high-temperature reservoir can be measured (by determining the amount of electrical energy required to maintain the temperature, for example), and the amount of heat given off to the low-temperature reservoir can be similarly determined (perhaps by finding the amount of ice melted, which may be compared with the electrical energy requirements to melt the same amount of ice). But from equations 2 and 3 we find that the ratio of these two quantities of heat defines the ratio of the two temperatures:

$$-\frac{q_1}{q_2} = \frac{T_1}{T_2} \tag{7}$$

If the experiment were done carefully, including proper attention to minimizing friction, we would find the ratio of the absolute temperatures of the boiling point and freezing point of water to be 1.366. Setting $T_1 = 1.366\, T_2$ and $\Delta T = T_1 - T_2$, it follows that

$$T_2 = \Delta T/(1.366 - 1) = 2.73\, \Delta T$$
$$T_1 = 3.73\, \Delta T$$

We are still free to choose ΔT, the number of degrees between the freezing point and boiling point, which determines the size of the degree of temperature. We could define the Kelvin scale by letting $\Delta T = 100°$K. Then $T_2 = 273°$K.[2] The Rankine scale is the absolute temperature scale in which there are 180°R between the freezing point and boiling point of

---

[2] In practice it has been found preferable to define the triple point of water—the temperature at which pure water is in equilibrium with pure ice under a pressure equal to the vapor pressure of the water and ice at that temperature—to be 273.16°K; then the difference between the freezing point and boiling point is measured to be 100°K. See H. F. Stimson, *J. Res. N. B. S.* **65**, 139 (1961).

water, as in the Fahrenheit scale. The zero of the Fahrenheit scale is
459.67°R.

NERNST'S HEAT THEOREM.   The entropy change for a chemical reaction
at a temperature T_2 can be found if the entropy change at some other temperature, T_1, is known and the heat capacities of reactants and products
are known. The procedure is analogous to Kirchhoff's law (equation 17,
Chapter 1). For a constant pressure,

$$\Delta S_2 = \int_{T_2}^{T_1} \frac{C_P(\text{reactants})}{T} \, dT + \Delta S_1 + \int_{T_1}^{T_2} \frac{C_P(\text{products})}{T} \, dT \qquad (8)$$

On the basis of measurements of entropies of reaction near room temperature, combined with measurements of heat capacities over a range of
temperatures, Nernst observed that calculated entropies of reaction seemed
to go to zero as the temperature approached zero. This observation provided the basis for a generalization known as *the third law of thermodynamics.*

There are several ways of stating the third law, and many of the implications are best understood from the standpoint of quantum statistical
mechanics. For present purposes the following statement will suffice:
*Every substance in its lowest energy state, at absolute zero, has the same
entropy.*

The third law cannot be demonstrated by carrying out chemical reactions
at 0°K. In the first place it is impossible to achieve absolute zero, and in
the second, the rates of chemical reactions decrease so rapidly with decreas-
ing temperature that few, if any, chemical reactions could proceed at temperatures even near 0°K. It is therefore necessary to rely on *calculated*
entropies of reaction, but it is now known that such calculated values
include many "apparent exceptions" to the third law, as might be expected
from the following argument.

Assume that a substance has an energy state that differs only slightly in
energy (or enthalpy) from the lowest energy state, but that this upper
energy state has an appreciable entropy difference from the lowest state.
Labeling the upper state with an asterisk and the lowest state with a subscript zero, $H^* - H_0$ is positive but very small, whereas $S^* - S_0$ is positive and not vanishingly small. Then, at a temperature greater than 0°K,
$T(S^* - S_0)$ may be greater than $H^* - H_0$, and the free-energy change for
the transition to the upper state will be negative, so that the system will
exist predominantly in the upper state. Only for vanishingly small temperatures will the enthalpy term be able to overcome the entropy term and make
the lowest energy state most stable, but at such low temperatures the time
required for the change of state may be so great that the lowest energy
state is never achieved experimentally.

From a knowledge of the structure of a substance, together with an
understanding of statistical mechanics, it is possible to predict which substances are likely to be "apparent exceptions" to the third law and to calculate the exact amount of the discrepancy to be expected. The excellent
agreement obtained between theory and experiment on the "exceptions"

is perhaps more impressive in showing the validity of the original postulate than is the much larger amount of experimental evidence obtained on substances that follow the simple expectations.

Entropy is a measure of disorder in a system and its evaluation depends upon a counting operation, so the entropy differences between states are often expressible as functions of small integers. Energies, however, may be arbitrarily close. Energy states that are very close together are said to be "degenerate" or "nearly degenerate." An example of near degeneracy of energy levels is provided by carbon monoxide, CO, which can pack in a solid crystal in the perfectly ordered arrangement CO CO CO or in disordered arrangements, such as CO CO OC CO, in which some molecules are turned around. Although these have only slightly different energies, there are so many possible disordered states that the equilibrium entropy at temperatures slightly above zero is[3] $R \ln 2 = 1.4$ cal/mole-deg above the entropy of the ground state, and this disorder remains, "frozen in," as the temperature is lowered toward zero.

Another form of degeneracy arises from the presence of small magnetic effects of the nuclei (associated with nuclear "spins"). The magnetic field of the earth is so weak that the nuclear magnets are not well aligned with each other. This has a negligible effect on the energy, but again a very appreciable effect on the entropy. However, since the nuclei are unchanged in a chemical reaction, there is no entropy change in a chemical reaction arising from these nuclear magnetic effects. The nuclear effects therefore do not cause an apparent exception to the third law. Because the "spin" state does not change, it may be called a "frozen" metastable equilibrium state, or a pseudoequilibrium state.

The third law may be restated, explicitly recognizing the existence of nonequilibrium states, as follows:

$$\operatorname*{Lim}_{T \to 0} \Delta S = 0$$

for any isothermal process involving only phases in internal equilibrium or involving any phase in a pseudoequilibrium state, provided the process does not disturb this pseudoequilibrium.

The importance of the third law, for classical thermodynamics, is that it provides a natural reference level[4] from which entropies can be measured and tabulated. These "absolute" entropies are available in handbooks, based on measurements of heat capacities from low temperatures. A few such values are given in Table 1. Tabulated entropies can be added or subtracted to find entropies of reaction, which can be combined with enthalpies of reaction to calculate free energies of reaction, and hence equilibrium constants. Entropies can also be calculated, employing equations of statis-

---

[3] The entropy depends on the number of possible molecular arrangements that the equilibrium state comprises. For each CO molecule there are two possible positions, so for one mole (N molecules) there are $(2)^N$ possibilities. The entropy is $k \ln 2^N = Nk \ln 2 = R \ln 2$.

[4] This reference level is often called *zero entropy*, but that name is somewhat misleading. No absolute value for entropy can be predicted from classical thermodynamics, and there is no way in which an absolute value of entropy could be meaningfully employed. The so-called "zero of entropy" is usually not the lowest entropy state attainable, for it ignores the spin effects mentioned above.

Table 1 STANDARD ENTROPIES, 25°C

Compound	State	$S°$ (cal/mole-deg)	Compound	State	$S°$ (cal/mole-deg)
Al	c	6.77	NO	g	50.35
$AlCl_3$	c	26.45	NO_2	g	57.34
Al_2O_3	c (α)	12.17	N_2O_4	c	35.92
Br_2	l	36.38		l	50.01
	g	58.65		g	72.72
C	graphite	1.36	HNO_3	g	63.66
	diamond	0.58	NH_3	g	45.97
CO	g	47.21	Na	c	12.30
CO_2	g	51.07	NaCl	c	17.24
CS_2	g	56.83	NaOH	c	15.34
Cl_2	g	53.29	O_2	g	49.00
F_2	g	48.45	O_3	g	57.08
H_2	g	31.21	P	red	5.45
HBr	g	47.44		white	9.82
HCl	g	44.65	PH_3	g	50.24
HF	g	41.51	S	rhombic	7.63
HI	g	49.35	SF_6	g	69.71
H_2O	g	45.11	SO_2	g	59.30
H_2O_2	g	55.66	CBr_4	g	85.56
H_2S	g	49.15	CCl_4	g	74.04
I_2	c	27.76	CF_4	g	62.46
	g	62.28	CH_4	g	44.49
K	c	15.46	C_2H_2	g	48.00
KCl	c	19.73	C_2H_4	g	52.45
KOH	c	18.96	C_2H_6	g	54.85
Mg	c	7.81	CH_3OH	g	56.8
MgO	c	6.44		l	30.3
$MgCl_2$	c	21.48	C_2H_5OH	g	67.4
MgF_2	c	13.68		l	38.4
N_2	g	45.77	C_6H_6	l	64.3
N_2O	g	52.55			

tical mechanics, if the molecular properties are known from spectroscopic measurements.

ATTAINMENT OF ABSOLUTE ZERO.[5] As we have seen, the most efficient refrigeration system is a reversible heat pump. The work required to withdraw an amount of heat $q = -q_2$ from a low-temperature reservoir at T_2 is, from equation 6,

$$w = \frac{\Delta T}{T_2} q \qquad (9)$$

As T_2 goes to zero, therefore, the amount of work required to remove a given amount of heat from any substance at the temperature T_2 will become infinite. It thus appears that the second law prohibits us from reaching the absolute zero.

A more meaningful equation for our purposes is obtained by finding the

---

[5] See E. M. Loebl, *J. Chem. Ed.* **37**, 361–363 (1960), and R. Fowler and E. A. Guggenheim, *Statistical Thermodynamics,* Cambridge, 1939, pp. 224–227.

work required for a given change in temperature. Replacing δq with $C_P\,dT$, the differential form of equation 9 becomes

$$\delta w = \frac{C_P}{T_2} \Delta T\,dT \qquad (10)$$

in which δw is the amount of work required to change the temperature of a substance, with heat capacity C_P, from the temperature T_2 to the temperature $T_2 - dT$, and ΔT is the difference in temperature between the substance and the surroundings. If the ratio C_P/T_2 becomes infinite, as might be expected, when T_2 goes to zero, the amount of work required for any given temperature change of the substance would indeed be infinite. It has been found, experimentally, however, that C_P also goes to zero as the temperature approaches $0°K$, and in fact the ratio C_P/T_2 becomes zero, rather than infinite. Therefore, we cannot argue that the second law prohibits us from reaching absolute zero.

If C_P/T_2 does go to zero as T_2 goes to zero, as observed experimentally and predicted from theory, then equation 8 can be applied to find entropies at the absolute zero. (The integral is not defined unless C_P/T remains finite.) Then it becomes possible to show that the third law of thermodynamics prohibits us from reaching absolute zero.

The proof is as follows. Let A and B represent any two phases that differ in some respect but which may be interconverted. For example, A and B might represent reactants and products for a chemical reaction, or they might represent two different crystalline modifications of a given chemical substance. Then the entropy of A at T_1 may be related to the entropy at absolute zero by the equation

$$S_A(T_1) = S_A^\circ + \int_0^{T_1} C_P(A)\,\frac{dT}{T}$$

and similarly, for phase B, the entropy at any temperature T_2 is

$$S_B(T_2) = S_B^\circ + \int_0^{T_2} C_P(B)\,\frac{dT}{T}$$

For every temperature, T_2, of phase B there must be a temperature, T_1, of phase A such that $S_A(T_1) = S_B(T_2)$:

$$S_A(T_1) = S_A^\circ + \int_0^{T_1} C_P(A)\,\frac{dT}{T} = S_B^\circ + \int_0^{T_2} C_P(B)\frac{dT}{T} = S_B(T_2)$$

Rearranging, we obtain

$$S_B^\circ - S_A^\circ = \int_0^{T_1} C_P(A)\,\frac{dT}{T} - \int_0^{T_2} C_P(B)\,\frac{dT}{T}$$

We may assume $T_1 \geqslant T_2$; if this is not satisfied we need only relabel the phases A and B to make it so.

Because the transformation from A, at T_1, to B, at T_2, is "isentropic" (no entropy change), it should be possible, in principle, to achieve an adiabatic, reversible transformation,

$$A(T_1) \longrightarrow B(T_2)$$

We are free to choose either T_1 or T_2; we choose to let $T_2 = 0$. Then either $T_1 > 0$ or $T_1 = 0$. If $T_1 > 0$, then

$$\int_0^{T_1} C_P(A) \frac{dT}{T} > 0 \quad \text{and} \quad S_B{}^\circ > S_A{}^\circ$$

but this would be a violation of the third law, which says that A and B must have the same entropy at absolute zero.

The only other possibility is that $T_1 = 0$. That is, the transition

$$A(T_1) \longrightarrow B(0)$$

can occur only if T_1 is zero; one cannot reach absolute zero from a non-zero temperature. The same argument may be turned around. If $S_B{}^\circ$ were greater than $S_A{}^\circ$, then T_1 would be greater than zero and it would be possible to reach absolute zero. If T_1 must be zero, then it follows that $S_A{}^\circ = S_B{}^\circ$.

Therefore, the following statement may be considered as an alternative form for the third law of thermodynamics: *It is impossible by any procedure, no matter how idealized, to reduce any system to the absolute zero in a finite number of operations.*

Suggested Further Reading

1. Mahan, Bruce H., *Elementary Chemical Thermodynamics,* Benjamin, New York, 1963.
2. Nash, Leonard K., *Elements of Chemical Thermodynamics,* Addison-Wesley, Reading, Mass., 1962.
3. Waser, Jurg, *Chemical Thermodynamics,* Benjamin, New York, 1965.
4. Moore, Walter J., *Physical Chemistry,* 3rd ed., Prentice-Hall, Englewood Cliffs, N.J., 1962.
5. Lewis, G. N., and Randall, M., *Thermodynamics and the Free Energy of Chemical Substances,* McGraw-Hill, New York, 1923. Lewis, G. N., Randall, M., Pitzer, K. S., and Brewer, L., *Thermodynamics,* 2nd ed., McGraw-Hill, 1961.
6. Sillen, L. G., Lange, P. W., and Gabrielson, C. O., *Problems in Physical Chemistry,* Prentice-Hall, Englewood Cliffs, N.J., 1952.
7. Adamson, Arthur W., *Understanding Physical Chemistry,* Benjamin, New York, 1964.
8. Brillouin, L., "Thermodynamics, Statistics, and Information," *Am. J. Phys.* **29,** 318–328 (1961).

Also see the Resource Paper on Elementary Chemical Thermodynamics by L. K. Nash, *J. Chem. Ed.* **42,** 64–75 (1965).

Appendix

Basic Operations of Calculus

Many problems of physics, chemistry, and engineering require an understanding not only of the operations of calculus but also of the justification and the limitations for these operations. Such questions are properly treated in mathematics tests. This appendix is in no way a substitute for such a rigorous development of calculus. It is, rather, a temporary expedient to allow the student who has not yet reached some of these operations in his mathematics studies to apply those particularly simple operations that are required in elementary thermodynamics.

NATURAL LOGARITHMS.   The common logarithms most often employed for computations are logarithms to the base 10. In certain types of mathematics, including calculus, it is more convenient to employ logarithms to the base $e = 2.71828\ldots$. These are called "natural" logarithms, and are often distinguished from the common (base 10) logarithms by the notation $\log_e x = \ln x$; $\log_{10} x = \log x$. Recalling that a logarithm is an exponent, it should be clear that natural logarithms are necessarily larger than common logarithms. For example, $e^{2.3} = 10$, $10^1 = 10$; therefore $\ln 10 = 2.3$, $\log 10 = 1$, and, quite generally,

$$\ln x = 2.30 \log x \tag{1}$$

Both the number e and the conversion factor $(2.3025851\ldots)$ are irrational numbers, which can be expressed to any number of decimal places. The number e may be defined as the limiting value, for small values of x, of the function $(1 + x)^{1/x}$, and therefore $(1/x)\ln(1 + x) = \ln e = 1$, or $\ln(1 + x) = x$ for sufficiently small values of x. A few representative logarithms are given in Table 1.

Computations with logarithm tables are generally more convenient with common logs, but slide rule calculations are often most easily performed if the logarithms that appear as natural logs are manipulated without conversion. Information concerning the LL (natural logarithm) scales can be found in the manufacturers' literature or in books devoted to slide rule methods.

Table 1   COMMON AND NATURAL LOGARITHMS

N	$\log N$	$\ln N$	N	$\log N$	$\ln N$
0.001	$\bar{3}.00000$	-6.9078	2	0.30103	0.6931
0.5	$\bar{1}.69897$	-0.6931	5	0.69897	1.6094
0.9	$\bar{1}.95424$	-0.1054	10	1	2.3026
0.995	$\bar{1}.99782$	-0.0050	20	1.30103	2.9957
1	0	0	500	2.69897	6.2146
1.005	0.00217	0.0050	2×10^{16}	16.30103	36.8041

APPENDIX

FUNCTIONAL NOTATION. Whenever the value of one quantity, or variable, depends on the value of some other quantity, or variable, the first variable is said to be a function of the second. This is often written $y = f(x)$, y equals f of x, to indicate that y is a function of x. For example, the area of a circle is a function of the radius. $A = f(r)$, where $f(r) = \pi r^2$. The symbol $f(\ )$ may be considered a "mold" into which the variable is placed. That is, if $f(x) = 3x^2 - 2x + 5$, then $f(z) = 3z^2 - 2z + 5$ and $f(a) = 3a^2 - 2a + 5$.

When several different functions are to be considered we can give each a different symbol. Thus the area of a circle, the temperature in degrees Kelvin, and the distance traveled by a falling object could be written $A = f(r)$, $T = g(t)$, and $s = h(v_i, t)$, with $f(r) = \pi r^2$, $g(t) = t + 273.15$ (t in $^\circ$C), and $h(v_i, t) = v_i t + \frac{1}{2}gt^2$. A much more convenient way to label these functions is to utilize the symbol of the quantity to be found. That is, we would write $A = A(r)$, $T = T(t)$, and $s = s(v_i, t)$, with $A(r) = \pi r^2$, $T(t) = t + 273.15$, and $s(v_i, t) = v_i t + \frac{1}{2}gt^2$. An equation such as $s = s(v_i, t)$ is not completely trivial. It says, in compact form, that "the distance traveled by a falling body depends on the initial velocity and on the time."

DERIVATIVES AND DIFFERENTIALS. An equation usually relates two or more variables, showing the values assumed by one quantity as the other variable, or variables, take on different possible values. For example, the pressure, volume, and temperature of an ideal gas are related by the equation

$$PV = nRT \tag{2}$$

in which n is the number of moles of gas, R is a universal constant (independent of which real gas is being considered, to the approximation that the real gas follows this equation), and the temperature is an "absolute" temperature, for which we will use the Kelvin scale.

One of the important questions that can be answered from such an equation concerns the rate at which one variable changes with changes in another. For example, we may ask how the volume changes with changes in temperature, for a fixed pressure. We can write

$$V_1 = \left(\frac{nR}{P}\right)T_1$$

$$V_2 = \left(\frac{nR}{P}\right)T_2$$

and therefore

$$\Delta V = V_2 - V_1 = \left(\frac{nR}{P}\right)(T_2 - T_1) = \left(\frac{nR}{P}\right)\Delta T$$

or

$$\frac{\Delta V}{\Delta T} = \frac{nR}{P} \tag{3}$$

It can be seen from Figure 1 that this is simply the slope of the line of volume plotted against temperature.

Now suppose that we are interested, instead, in how volume changes with pressure, at a fixed temperature. This curve, a hyperbola, is shown in Figure 2. It is clear that the slope is no longer constant. Proceeding as before, we write

$$V_1 = nRT(1/P_1)$$

$$V_2 = nRT(1/P_2)$$

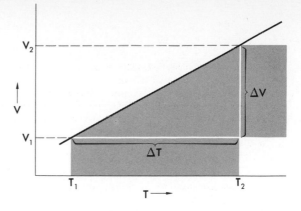

FIGURE 1 *Volume against temperature for an ideal gas. The slope of the line is* $\Delta V/\Delta T = nR/P.$

and subtracting we obtain

$$\Delta V = V_2 - V_1 = nRT(1/P_2 - 1/P_1) = nRT(P_1 - P_2)/P_1P_2 = nRT\frac{-\Delta P}{P_1P_2}$$

$$\frac{\Delta V}{\Delta P} = \frac{-nRT}{P_1P_2} \tag{4}$$

This calculated value is not the slope of the curve at either P_1, V_1 or P_2, V_2; it is the slope of the chord connecting these two points. Thus the slope depends not only on where we start (P_1, V_1) but also on how far we go. If we want the slope at the point P_1, V_1—that is, the slope of the line tangent to the curve at this point—we can take P_2 closer and closer to P_1. If P_2 is sufficiently close to P_1, we can write equation 4 in the form

$$\left.\frac{\Delta V}{\Delta P}\right)_{P=P_1} = -\frac{nRT}{P_1{}^2} \tag{5}$$

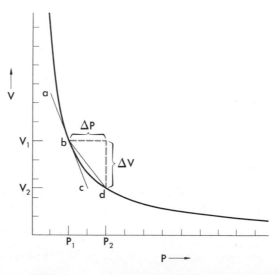

FIGURE 2 *Volume against pressure for an ideal gas. The slope of the chord, bd, is* $\Delta V/\Delta P = -nRT/P_1P_2.$ *The slope of the tangent at b, ac, is* $dV/dP = -nRT/P_1{}^2.$

Table 2   BASIC DERIVATIVES

Function	Derivative
$y = u + v$	$dy/dx = du/dx + dv/dx$
$y = x^n$	$dy/dx = nx^{n-1}$
$y = v^n$	$dy/dx = nv^{n-1}\, dv/dx$
$y = uv$	$dy/dx = v\, du/dx + u\, dv/dx$
$y = \ln x$	$dy/dx = 1/x$
$y = e^v$	$dy/dx = e^v\, dv/dx$
$y = a$ (constant)	$dy/dx = 0$

Table 3   ADDITIONAL DERIVATIVES

Equation	Derivatives
$y = ax$	$dy/dx = a$
$y = ax^2$	$dy/dx = 2ax$
$y = a/x$	$dy/dx = -a/x^2$
$y = ax^{-n}$	$dy/dx = -nax^{-(n+1)}$
$y = u/v$	$dy/dx = (1/v)\, du/dx - (u/v^2)\, dv/dx$
	$\qquad = \dfrac{v\, du/dx - u\, dv/dx}{v^2}$
$y = e^{ax}$	$dy/dx = ae^{ax}$
$y = x \ln x$	$dy/dx = \ln x + 1$
$V = nRT/P$	$dV/dT = nR/P$ (P constant)
$E = 1/2mv^2$	$dE/dv = mv$
$V = nRT/P$	$dV/dP = -nRT/P^2$ (T constant)
$f = q_1q_2/r^2$	$df/dr = -2q_1q_2/r^3$
$v_f = \sqrt{v_o^2 + 2as}$	$dv_f/ds = 1/2(v_o^2 + 2as)^{-1/2}(2a)$
	$\qquad = a/\sqrt{v_o^2 + 2as}$

This says that the slope of the line tangent to the curve at P_1, V_1 depends on P_1, as it should by inspection of the curve, but not on any other pressure value, which is also quite reasonable.

The slope of the line tangent to a curve is called the "derivative" of the curve, and is written in the form dy/dx.[1] These derivatives cannot always be found as easily as for the two examples considered above, but for present purposes only a very few formulas are required, and these few are given in Table 2.

From these few basic expressions it is possible to obtain many others. A few of these are listed in Table 3. The student should check each of these himself by applying the formulas from Table 2.

For many purposes the derivative may be considered as an ordinary fraction, or ratio, of two very small quantities, called "differentials." Thus, for an infinitesimal[2] change in any variable there will be a corresponding small change in any function depending on that variable. We could write, for example (compare equations 3 and 5 and Table 3),

[1] The derivative is defined as the limiting value of the ratio $\Delta y/\Delta x$ as Δx becomes small.

$$dy/dx = \lim_{\Delta x \to 0} \frac{\Delta y}{\Delta x}$$

[2] The word "infinitesimal" means roughly that it is smaller than any specific number with which it may be compared. For present purposes, those who have not yet been introduced to the theory of limits may substitute "sufficiently small" for the word "infinitesimal."

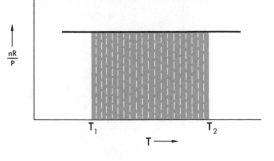

FIGURE 3 *The product $\frac{nR}{P}\Delta T_j$ is the area of the jth rectangle and the sum of all these rectangles is the total volume change.*

$$dV = \frac{nR}{P}\,dT \qquad (P \text{ constant}) \tag{6}$$

$$dV = \frac{-nRT}{P^2}\,dP \qquad (T \text{ constant}) \tag{7}$$

$$dE = mv\,dv \tag{8}$$

$$dy = \frac{dy}{dx}\,dx \tag{9}$$

SUMS AND INTEGRALS.   The total change in volume of a gas with change in temperature, at a constant pressure, can be considered as the sum of small changes with small changes in temperature. This can be written

$$\Delta V = V_f - V_i = \frac{nR}{P}(\Delta T_1 + \Delta T_2 + \Delta T_3 + \cdots + \Delta T_f)$$

$$\Delta V = \sum_{j=1}^{j=f} (\Delta V)_j = \sum_{j=1}^{j=f} \frac{nR}{P}\Delta T_j \tag{10}$$

If we plot nR/P (which is constant) against temperature (Figure 3), the volume change can be considered as the sum of the areas of the rectangles of height nR/P and width ΔT_j. The total volume change is the area under the curve between the limits T_1 and T_2.

The change in volume with change in pressure, at a constant temperature, also can be represented as a sum of small changes, but more care is required. In particular, if $-nRT/P^2$ is plotted against P, the area under the curve, between P_1 and P_2, will give the total volume change, but this is only approximately a sum over finite increments. It is necessary to make the steps very small to follow the shape of the curve properly (Figure 4). An exactly correct answer is obtained if we sum over the differentials. This could be written

$$\sum_j dV_j = \sum_j \frac{-nRT}{P_j^2}\,dP_j$$

but because the differentials are infinitesimals, an infinite number of them are required, and therefore we introduce the $\int$ sign to contrast this type of sum from the conventional sum, Σ, over larger fixed increments. The sum, or "integral," is then written

$$\Delta V = V_f - V_i = \int_{V_i}^{V_f} dV = \int_{P_i}^{P_f} \frac{-nRT}{P^2}\,dP = \frac{nRT}{P_f} - \frac{nRT}{P_i} \tag{11}$$

111

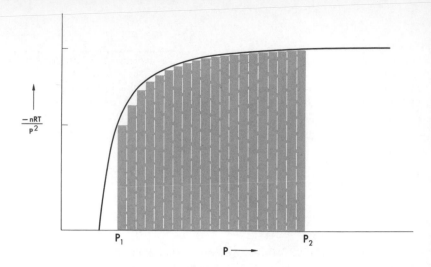

We could have written, similarly, for equation 10,

$$\Delta V = V_f - V_i = \int_{V_i}^{V_f} dV = \int_{T_i}^{T_f} \frac{nR}{P}\, dT = \frac{nRT_f}{P} - \frac{nRT_i}{P} \tag{12}$$

It should be noted that in both equation 11 and equation 12, the "integrands" (the quantities appearing "inside" the integrals—that is, after the integral sign) are the differentials of the terms appearing in the answers, or integrals. This is necessarily true. Integration and differentiation are therefore said to be inverse processes with respect to each other. We usually evaluate an integral by asking "What function could we take the differential of to obtain this integrand?" Extensive tables of integrals are available, but for present purposes only the few given in Table 4 are required.

Table 4   BASIC INTEGRALS

$$\int_{x_1}^{x_2} dx = x_2 - x_1$$

$$\int_{x_1}^{x_2} x^n\, dx = \frac{1}{n+1} x_2{}^{n+1} - \frac{1}{n+1} x_1{}^{n+1} \quad (n \neq -1)$$

$$\int_{x_1}^{x_2} \frac{dx}{x} = \ln x_2 - \ln x_1 = \ln x_2/x_1$$

$$\int_{x_1}^{x_2} e^{ax}\, dx = \frac{1}{a} e^{ax_2} - \frac{1}{a} e^{ax_1}$$

$$\int_{x_1}^{x_2} (u + v)\, dx = \int_{x_1}^{x_2} u\, dx + \int_{x_1}^{x_2} v\, dx$$

$$\int_{x_1}^{x_2} d[u(x)] = u(x_2) - u(x_1)$$

FUNCTIONS OF MORE THAN ONE VARIABLE. In the preceding sections we have treated changes of only one variable at a time. One of the important results of calculus is that, so long as we consider only infinitesimal changes, or differentials, changes in more than one variable are simply additive. For example, given $V = nRT/P$,

$$dV = \frac{nR}{P} dT + (-nRT/P^2) dP$$

or, more generally, if u is a function of $x, y, z, \ldots$, and $x, y, z, \ldots$ are independent of each other, then

$$du = \frac{du}{dx}\bigg)_{y,z\ldots} dx + \frac{du}{dy}\bigg)_{x,z\ldots} dy + \frac{du}{dz}\bigg)_{x,y\ldots} dz + \cdots$$

where the first derivative is found by assuming all of the independent variables except x are considered constant, the second derivative considers all except y constant, and so forth as noted by the subscripts on the parentheses. To indicate more clearly that one or more variables are being considered constant, these derivatives are customarily written

$$du = \frac{\partial u}{\partial x}\bigg)_{y,z\ldots} dx + \frac{\partial u}{\partial y}\bigg)_{x,z\ldots} dy + \frac{\partial u}{\partial z}\bigg)_{x,y\ldots} dz + \cdots \tag{13}$$

In such an expression the changes of independent variables, dx, dy, dz, etc., are called differentials, as in preceding sections. The change in u, du, is called the total differential of u, and the derivatives, $\partial u/\partial x$, $\partial u/\partial y$, etc., are called partial derivatives.

Problems

1. Obtain a good estimate of $(1.0005)^5$ employing natural logarithms, but without looking up logs or antilogs.
2. The maximum of a function can be found from the condition that the slope (and hence the derivative) is zero at a maximum or minimum. Find the maximum of the function $y = 5 - 3(x + 2)^2$ by finding dy/dx and then setting this new function (the derivative) equal to zero.
3. The area of a rectangle, of perimeter p, is hw with $p = 2(h + w)$. Therefore $h = p/2 - w$ and $A = w(p/2 - w)$. Find the width, w, that will give the maximum area (see problem 2) for a fixed value of p.
4. Force is mass times acceleration, or mass times the rate of change of velocity with time, dv/dt. Show that the integral of force over distance, $\int f\,dx$, can be rewritten $\int mv\,dv$, because velocity is the rate of change of distance with time, dx/dt. Show that the work done on a particle, $\int f\,dx$, is equal to the increase in kinetic energy, $\frac{1}{2}mv^2$, of the particle.
5. Show that a Coulombic force, $f = q_1q_2/r^2$, acting over a distance r, gives the expression for potential energy between charged particles. P.E. $= -q_1q_2/r$, when the limiting values of r are taken as infinity and r (that is, an arbitrary value, r, to be specified later).

Answers to Problems

1. a. 0.029 b. 0.094 c. 35 cal
2. 33°C
3. a. 55,000/102,000 b. 1330/2460
   c. 5570/10,300; $\Delta E = 0$
4. $q = w = 240$ cal
5. 65.3°C
6. a. 6650 cal/mole b. 9.5%
7. $-70,960$ cal/mole;
   $-103,780$ cal/mole
8. $\Delta H = -23,510$ cal/mole; $\Delta E = -23,210$ cal/mole
9. 607,400 cal
10. Measure heats of combustion and subtract
11. 565 cal/gm
12. $-33,280$ cal/mole
13. $-51,340$ cal/mole
14. 28.8; 1.18
15. S_2F_2
16. 32.8 atm
17. 32.1 atm
18. $V = 9.77$ L
19. a. 3×10^{13} b. 3×10^7
    c. 3×10^{-17}

1. Water rises because of adhesion to the capillary and therefore will not drip from an opening.
2. Magnetic shields become magnetized and distort the magnetic field.
3. 9.2 cal/deg
4. a. 6.89 cal/deg b. 6.89 cal/deg
   c. 13.78 cal/deg d. 0
5. $n_1R \ln (V_1 + V_2)/V_1 + n_2R \ln (V_1 + V_2)/V_2 = -n_1R \ln N_1 - n_2R \ln N_2 = -n(N_1R \ln N_1 + N_2R \ln N_2)$
6. a. 20.65 cal/deg b. 1.685 cal/deg; first process (6a) can be broken into two steps: equilibration of pressures by movement of a piston separating the two volumes ($\Delta S = 1.685$ cal/deg) followed by mixing (as in 5, $\Delta S = 18.95$ cal/deg)
7. a. left b. right c. right d. left
8. The system (gas) is mechanically isolated and therefore can do work only on itself, not on surroundings.

9. -2725 cal; -2067 cal, -4134 cal; -6195 cal, -508.5 cal
10. a. 20.4 cal/mole-deg b. 0
11. 2120 cal
12. a. $-24,140$ cal b. -28.8 cal/deg
13. -33.9 cal/deg
14. a. $-138,200$; $-55,500$; $-75,900$ cal
    b. $-120,600$; $-46,500$; $-67,200$ cal
    c. -59.0; -30.2; -29.2 cal/deg. Fe_2O_3 is formed spontaneously from either of the others.
15. Less stable because $\Delta S < 0$ and so ΔG increases with T.
16. a. Unfavorably by increase of T, favorably by increase of P b. Increase of T increases rate, increase of P restores yield.
17. a. + b. − c. + d. + e. +
    f. − g. −. Sign of ΔS is generally determined by increase or decrease of moles of gas; decrease of number of independent molecules (polymerization) also decreases entropy.
18. a. 0 (-9 kcal for water, $+9$ kcal for ice) b. 2 cal/deg c. 7°C
19. a. 10.20 cal/deg b. 3875 cal
    c. 3615 cal
20. a. 8400 b. 2005
21. a. -375 cal b. -1.37 cal/deg
    c. -15 cal
22. a. -1100 cal b. 6.40 atm

CHAPTER 3

1. 14,700 atm
2. 90,200 cal/mole
3. Fugacity increases with P, more for ice than water because volume is slightly larger.
4. a. $-b/a$ b. $-bR$
5. $\frac{6}{17}, \frac{1}{17}, \frac{2}{17}, \frac{8}{17}$
6. 0.026 M
7. 0.00060; 0.0063 M; 0.0039 m
8. a. 55.55 M b. 55.55 m c. 10.30 M
   d. 6.5 m e. 0.0409 M
9. a. 0.650, 0.223, 0.126 b. 19.03 m, 10.80 m c. 63.5 m, 12.30 m
10. 100 torr (water layer is irrelevant at equilibrium)

11. a. 468 L-atm/mole or 2.60×10^4 atm   b. 950 L-atm/mole or 5.28×10^4 atm
12. Large. (Benzene is insoluble, therefore moderate P gives small concentration and P/c is large.)
13. a. 23%   b. 10.5%
14. a. 20.815 ml   b. 18 ml (45 ppm smaller than pure water)   c. 26.95 ml
15. 52.2 torr benzene, 22.6 torr toluene
16. a. $1.86 \times 10^{-3}°C$ b. $5.16 \times 10^{-4}°C$
    c. $1.8 \times 10^{-3}\%$ (4.27×10^{-4} torr)
    d. 25.3 cm
17. a. 733.7 torr   b. 11.3 torr   c. 98.5% water, 1.5% compound
18. S_8

CHAPTER 4

1. 1.27

2. a. $\dfrac{a_{CuS}(a_{H^+})^2}{a_{Cu^{++}}a_{H_2S}} \approx \dfrac{(C_{H^+})^2}{C_{Cu^{++}}C_{H_2S}}$

   b. $\dfrac{(a_{Hg})^2 a_{O_2}}{(a_{HgO})^2} \approx P_{O_2}$

   c. $\dfrac{a_{CO_2} a_{H_2O}}{a_{HCO_3^-} a_{H^+}} \approx \dfrac{P_{CO_2}}{C_{HCO_3^-} C_{H^+}}$

   d. $\dfrac{a_{AcOH} a_{EtOH}}{a_{AcOEt} a_{H_2O}} \approx \dfrac{C_{AcOH} N_{EtOH}}{N_{AcOEt}}$

3. $K = 5.6 \times 10^{17}$; $N_{C_6H_6} = 1.4 \times 10^{-20}$
4. No effect
5. Shift to right. (Inert gas dilutes out the reacting system, lowering partial pressures and causing a shift to the right to oppose the change. By differentiation,

   $$\dfrac{dn_{N_2O_4}}{dn_X} = \dfrac{-n_{N_2O_4}}{n_X + (4P/K + 1)n_{NO_2}}$$

   where n_X is number of moles of inert gas added.)
6. 9.6% (Suggestion for solution of cubic, $40.8x^3 + x - 5 = 0$; if $x = 0$, $f(x) = -5$; if $x = 1$, $f(x) = 36.8$, $\therefore 0 < x < 1 < 5$, so $40.8x^3 \approx 5$. This gives $x \approx 0.5$, and then $40.8x^3 = 4.5$, $x = 0.48$)
7. a. 1×10^{-8} b. 3×10^{-7} atm SO_2 (2.3×10^{-4} torr); 6×10^{-7} atm H_2S

8. $\frac{1}{4}$ atm SO_3, 3×10^{-9} atm SO_2; $1.2 \times 10^{-6}\%$ dissociation. [Suggestion for solution of cubic, $4x^3 = K(\frac{1}{4} - 2x)^2$; max. possible value for x is $\frac{1}{8}$, but K is very small, hence $x \ll \frac{1}{8}$ and $4x^3 \approx (\frac{1}{16})K$.]
9. a. -2570 cal; 11.9   b. -5140 cal; 140   c. $-\infty$ d. 0.855 atm
10. a. $1.21 \times 10^{-3} M$ b. $7.1 \times 10^{-5} M$
    c. increase
11. $+11,000$ cal; MgF_2 will not spontaneously dissolve sufficiently to reach the standard state (approx. 1 M).
12. a. $3.46 \times 10^{-4} M$ b. $4.70 \times 10^{-4} M$
    c. B goes into solution and A precipitates out   d. At equilibrium, two phases (plus vapor): solid A and solution
13. $9.55 \times 10^{-5} M$
14. a. $2.21 \times 10^{-4} M$ b. $6.30 \times 10^{-6} M$
15. a. $Zn + 2 Ag^+(0.5 M) \longrightarrow Zn^{++}(0.01 M) + 2 Ag$ b. 1.562 volt
    c. 1.603 volt   d. yes
16. 4.07
17. a. Decreased   b. increased
    c. cathode   d. left to right
18. 47,360 cal (198,330 joule)
19. a. $-31,000$ cal   b. $-33,500$ cal
    c. -8.02 cal/deg
20. 5.5
21. Protected by oxidation of Mg, reduction of iron oxides.
22. Ag^+
23. a. Hg^{++} b. Hg^{++} c. Hg_2^{++}

APPENDIX

1. $5 \times 0.0005 = 0.0025$
2. $dy/dx = -6(x + 2)$; maximum at $x = -2$
3. $w = h = p/4$

4. $\int f \, dx = \int m \dfrac{dv}{dt} \, dx =$

   $\int m \dfrac{dx}{dt} \, dv = \int mv \, dv =$

   $\frac{1}{2}mv_2^2 - \frac{1}{2}mv_1^2$

5. $\int \dfrac{q_1 q_2}{r^2} \, dr = \left[\dfrac{-q_1 q_2}{r} \right]_{r=r} -$

   $\left[\dfrac{-q_1 q_2}{r} \right]_{r=\infty} = \dfrac{-q_1 q_2}{r} - 0$

Index